Continued fractions
and their generalizations:
A short history of
f-expansions

FRITZ SCHWEIGER

Docent
Press

DOCENT PRESS
Boston, Massachusetts, USA
www.docentpress.com

Docent Press publishes books in the history of mathematics and computing about interesting people and intriguing ideas. The histories are told at many levels of detail and depth that can be explored at leisure by the general reader.

Cover design by Brenda Riddell, Graphic Details.

Table of Contents

Devoted to the memory of John Kinney

Preface

My first mathematical research considered the so-called Jacobi algorithm, a generalization of continued fractions. The topic was given me by Wolfgang Schmidt, one of my teachers. Later on Walter Philipp advised me to use ergodic theory for questions in this area. However, my mathematical interests were strongly influenced by John Kinney who invited me to spend almost a year at his place, East Lansing in Michigan. From this time on my mathematical research was centered around generalizations of continued fractions which we can call f-expansions and multidimensional continued fractions.

Therefore after some hesitation I followed the offer of Scott Guthery to write a book on the development of f-expansions in the last hundred years or so. This topic starts with elementary number theory but influenced the genesis of ergodic theory which is one of the tools to investigate the behavior of different algorithms and maps.

Salzburg, Spring 2015

Chapter 1

Introduction

Counting is an old cultural technique. For small numbers simple words which cannot be analyzed further are used, e. g. *one, two, three, ..., ten* in English and *un, deux, trois, ..., dix* in French. As a rule other techniques are employed to name higher numbers. Some of these words were formed centuries ago. Since languages have changed their formation is very often not entirely clear. *Eleven* comes from something like *one over (ten)* and *twelve* from *two over (ten)*. The number words *thirteen* to *nineteen* reflect addition $3 + 10$ to $9 + 10$, the number words *twenty* to *ninety* multiplication 2×10 to 9×10. New words are used for 100 and 1000. The word *million* comes from Italian *miglione*, literally 'great thousand'.

Things changed when writing was invented. The Romans used a stroke I for 1, two strokes II for 2, and so on. They wrote V for 5, X for 10, L for 50, and C for 100. This notation has a serious drawback. You cannot use it for written addition and multiplication. Try to multiply 28 times 61 written as XXVIII times LXI. Therefore merchants normally used a counting board (Latin *abacus* from Greek $\alpha\beta\alpha\xi$). It was a great invention when the so-called Indian notation was introduced by the Arabs. Since this notation was transmitted by the Arabs to Europe we call this notation Arabic digits. Here the idea of *recursion* is present, e. g. 243 stands for $2 \times 100 + 4 \times 10 + 3$. This device became very fruitful when it was used for decimal numbers, e. g. 14.813 means $1 \times 10 + 4 + 8 \times \frac{1}{10} + 1 \times \frac{1}{100} + 3 \times \frac{1}{1000}$.

The following *algorithm* can be given. Let x be a real number and denote by $\lfloor x \rfloor$ the *integral part* of x, i. e. the integer $\lfloor x \rfloor$ which satisfies

$$\lfloor x \rfloor \leq x < \lfloor x \rfloor + 1.$$

1

Then write
$$x = \lfloor x \rfloor + \theta,$$
where the number θ satisfies $0 \le \theta < 1$. We denote $\varepsilon_1 = \varepsilon_1(\theta) = \lfloor 10\theta \rfloor$ and form
$$\theta_1 = 10\theta - \varepsilon_1.$$
This gives us the representation
$$\theta = \frac{\varepsilon_1}{10} + \frac{\theta_1}{10}.$$
If we repeat this algorithm we write $\varepsilon_2 = \varepsilon_2(\theta) = \lfloor 10\theta_1 \rfloor$ and
$$\theta_2 = 10\theta_1 - \varepsilon_2$$
and find
$$\theta = \frac{\varepsilon_1}{10} + \frac{\varepsilon_2}{10^2} + \frac{\theta_2}{10^2}.$$
It is evident that we can repeat further which leads us to
$$\theta = \frac{\varepsilon_1}{10} + \frac{\varepsilon_2}{10^2} + \ldots + \frac{\varepsilon_N}{10^N} + \frac{\theta_N}{10^N}.$$
If we trust in *convergence* we then find
$$\theta = \sum_{j=1}^{\infty} \frac{\varepsilon_j}{10^j}.$$

This is one of the oldest examples of an f-expansion where we use the function $f(\theta) = 10\theta$. For more information on number words and the history of writing numbers the old classic [Menninger 1977] is still a good source although research during the last decades unearthed new insights (see e. g. [Mazur 2014]). Information and references about the linguistic theory of number words can be found in [Schweiger 1997].

This book is about the history of f-expansions, their theory, their application, and their connection to other parts of mathematics. Sketches of proofs of some of the theorems about f-expansions—particularly theorems from historical sources—are included not to convince you of the truth of the theorem but rather as a way to show you *why* the theorem is true. These sketches should give a clearer and more easily understood description of the working of the theorem than a hand-waving literary flourish. There are now several thousand papers connected with f-expansions. The book should serve as a lively and readable account and perhaps as an invitation to this area.

What we now call f-expansions has a long history. The forerunners are decimal expansions and continued fractions which clearly will be considered in this book. The choice $b = 10$ is the most common base for decimal expansions but note that the choice $b = 60$ goes back to Mesopotamian culture. It is still present when 1 hour equals 60 minutes and 1 minute equals 60 seconds. Later various other series expansions were proposed and the invention of continued fractions of several kinds is also quite ancient. The first proof of the irrationality of the circle number π can be found in [Lambert 1761] where continued fractions are employed (see [Perron 1957]). He used the identity

$$\tan \frac{m}{n} = \cfrac{m}{n - \cfrac{m^2}{3n - \cfrac{m^2}{5n - ...}}}.$$

In the last century f-expansions were invented and reinvented by several writers. It turned out that these expansions brought some new results in number theory but also in probability theory and ergodic theory.

As a kind of background theory we occasionally use the language of fibred systems [Schweiger 1995]. Let $B = \bigcup_{k \in I} B(k)$ be a partition (sometimes called the time-1-partition) and $T : B \to B$ be a map such that T is injective on each subset $B(k)$. Here I is a finite or countable set, called the set of *digits*. In most of our examples B is a subset of the real line $\mathbb{R}$. We further consider the space $\Omega = I^{\mathbb{N}}$, the space of all sequences $\omega = (\omega_1, \omega_2, \omega_3, ...)$, and the map

$$\tau(\omega_1, \omega_2, \omega_3, ...) = (\omega_2, \omega_3, \omega_4, ...)$$

which is called the *shift*. The map $\psi : B \to \Omega$ is defined by $\omega_n(\psi x) = k_n$ if $T^{n-1} x \in B(k_n)$. Then we see that $\tau(\psi x) = \psi(Tx)$.

For decimal expansions we can take $B = [0, 1[$, $B(k) = [\frac{k}{10}, \frac{k+1}{10}[$, $I = \{0, 1, ..., 9\}$, and $Tx = 10x - \lfloor 10x \rfloor$. For continued fractions we take $B = [0, 1] \setminus \mathbb{Q}$, $B(k) = [\frac{1}{k+1}, \frac{1}{k}[$, $I = \{1, 2, 3, ...\}$, and $Tx = \frac{1}{x} - \lfloor \frac{1}{x} \rfloor$.

A cylinder of rank s is the set

$$B(k_1, ..., k_s) = \{x \in B : k_1(x) = k_1, ..., k_s(x) = k_s\}.$$

Since T is injective on every cylinder there is an inverse map

$$V(k_1, ..., k_s) : T^s B(k_1, ..., k_s) \to B(k_1, ..., k_s).$$

If we use the metrical theory of fibred systems (this means probability theory or ergodic theory are applied to fibred systems) we assume that a measure λ

is given on the set B and the map T is *non-singular*, i. e. $\lambda(E) = 0$ implies $\lambda(T^{-1}E) = 0$. Then we can also define Jacobians $\omega(k_1, ..., k_s)$ by the equation

$$\int_{T^{-s}E \cap B(k_1, ..., k_s)} d\lambda = \int_E \omega(k_1, ..., k_s) d\lambda.$$

The notations vary greatly between different authors. No attempt was made to unify them but in almost all instances I use λ to denote Lebesgue measure. Furthermore $[a, b]$ denotes a closed interval and $]a, b[$ an open interval. Very often we use the notation of the authors which may give the feeling of coming closer to the original sources.

Chapter 2

Continued fractions

There are two prominent examples for f-expansions: *g-adic expansions* which arise from the function $f(x) = \frac{x}{g}$, $g \geq 2$ and *(regular) continued fractions* which arise from $f(x) = \frac{1}{x}$. Many books on number theory contain a chapter on continued fractions. A classic on continued fractions and various generalizations, i. e. continued fractions of the form

$$b_0 + \cfrac{a_1}{b_1 + \cfrac{a_2}{b_2 + \cfrac{a_3}{b_3 + ...}}}$$

is the book [Perron 1957, 1954]. The first volume deals with the number theoretical case where the quantities $b_0, a_1, b_1, a_2, b_2, ...$ are integers. In the second volume these quantities can also be functions of a real or complex variable which is in fact a different story. A continued fraction is called *regular* if b_0 is an integer, $b_n \geq 1$ are integers, and $a_n = 1$ for all $n \geq 1$. If the setting is clear the adjective 'regular' normally is dropped.

Perron's first volume gives a well readable account with a good bibliography which refers to all results presented in the book. A comprehensive survey of the historical development until 1939 is [Brezinski 1991]. Its scientific bibliography alone counts 2302 items! We further mention [Khintchine 1963], [Rockett and Szüsz 1996], [Iosifescu & Kraaikamp 2002], [Hensley 2006], [Karpenkov 2013] (its first part deals with the geometry of continued fractions, the second part is devoted to multidimensional generalizations), and [Borwein, van der Poorten, Shallit & Zudilin 2014].

We will shortly present some standard results following Khintchine's book. We

remark that Khintchine contributed much to the development of the metrical theory of continued fractions (e. g. [Khintchine 1936, 1935]).
If

$$a_0 + \cfrac{1}{a_1 + \cfrac{1}{a_2 + \dots}}$$

is a finite or infinite regular continued fraction then the numbers $a_0, a_1, a_1, \dots$ are called *elements* or *partial denominators* of the continued fraction. In the context of f-expansions the notion *digits* would also be appropriate. For regular continued fractions the notation $[a_0; a_1, a_2, \dots]$ is customary. The terminating fractions

$$a_0 + \cfrac{1}{a_1 + \cfrac{1}{a_2 + \dots + \cfrac{1}{a_n}}} = \frac{p_n}{q_n}$$

form *convergents* to a given number. The recursion relations are best expressed by matrices which are not used in Khintchine's book, but for n-dimensional generalizations matrices are very useful.

$$\begin{pmatrix} q_{k+1} & q_k \\ p_{k+1} & p_k \end{pmatrix} = \begin{pmatrix} q_k & q_{k-1} \\ p_k & p_{k-1} \end{pmatrix} \begin{pmatrix} a_{k+1} & 1 \\ 1 & 0 \end{pmatrix}, \ k \geq 0.$$

The start values are $q_0 = 1$, $p_0 = a_0$, $q_{-1} = 0$, $p_{-1} = 1$. It has long been known that

$$\frac{p_{n+1}}{q_{n+1}} < x < \frac{p_n}{q_n}, \ n = 1, 3, 5, \dots$$

and

$$\frac{1}{q_n(q_n + q_{n+1})} < \left| x - \frac{p_n}{q_n} \right| \leq \frac{1}{q_n q_{n+1}}.$$

It is easy to see that one can restrict to the case $0 < x < 1$. This leads to the (Gauss) map

$$Tx = \frac{1}{x} - \left\lfloor \frac{1}{x} \right\rfloor$$

which generates the continued fraction expansion. If $a_1 = a_1(x) = \lfloor \frac{1}{x} \rfloor$ then

$$x = \frac{1}{a_1 + Tx}.$$

Then one sees that the relation

$$x = \frac{p_n + p_{n-1} T^n x}{q_n + q_{n-1} T^n x}$$

is true for all $n \geq 0$.

The following results were the starting point for the research on the *Lagrange spectrum*. Let $k \geq 1$ then at least one of the two inequalities are true

$$\left| x - \frac{p_k}{q_k} \right| \leq \frac{1}{2q_k^2}.$$

$$\left| x - \frac{p_{k+1}}{q_{k+1}} \right| \leq \frac{1}{2q_{k+1}^2}.$$

Furthermore at least one of the three following inequalities is true

$$\left| x - \frac{p_k}{q_k} \right| \leq \frac{1}{\sqrt{5}q_k^2}.$$

$$\left| x - \frac{p_{k+1}}{q_{k+1}} \right| \leq \frac{1}{\sqrt{5}q_{k+1}^2}$$

$$\left| x - \frac{p_{k+2}}{q_{k+2}} \right| \leq \frac{1}{\sqrt{5}q_{k+1}^2}.$$

This result is best possible. If

$$\alpha == \cfrac{1}{1 + \cfrac{1}{1 + ...}} = \frac{1}{1 + \alpha}$$

then

$$\lim_{n \to \infty} q_n |\alpha q_n - p_n| = \frac{1}{\sqrt{5}}.$$

This result essentially goes back to [Hurwitz 1891]. Later [Bagemihl & McLaughlin 1966] generalized this result in replacing $\sqrt{5}$ by $\sqrt{a_{k+2}^2 + 4}$. [Tong 1983] showed a kind of conjugate property, namely that for at least one $j \in \{0, 1, 2\}$ we have

$$\left| x - \frac{p_{k+j}}{q_{k+j}} \right| > \frac{1}{q_{k+j}^2 \sqrt{a_{k+2}^2 + 4}}.$$

Such results can be further generalized and extended to other types of continued fractions. [Jager & Kraaikamp 1989] showed that for *continued fractions to the nearest integer* the Hurwitz constant $\sqrt{5}$ should be replaced by $\frac{5}{2}(5\sqrt{5} - 11)$ (see also [Tong 1994]).

Let us call two real numbers α and β *equivalent* if these two numbers have the same continued fraction expansion from a certain point onwards. It is known that two numbers α and β are equivalent if

$$\alpha = \frac{A\beta + B}{C\beta + D}, \text{ where } A, B, C, D \in \mathbb{Z}, \text{ and } |AD - BC| = 1.$$

Let us denote by

$$L(\alpha) = \liminf_{n} q_n |q_n\alpha - p_n|$$

then equivalence of α and β implies $L(\alpha) = L(\beta)$. The numbers $L(\alpha)$, $\alpha \in \mathbb{R}\backslash\mathbb{Q}$, form the *Lagrange spectrum*. The smallest value is $\sqrt{5}$. The next values are $\sqrt{8}$, ... with the number 3 as its first limit point. A good introduction can be found in [Cassels 1957]. More recent developments can be found in [Pollington & Moran 1993].

Another idea was to consider the sequence of constants C_n defined by

$$x - \frac{p_n}{q_n} = \frac{(-1)^n}{C_n q_n q_{n+1}}.$$

Put

$$D_n = \frac{1}{C_n - 1}.$$

An essential tool is the study of the *natural extension* which we will consider in connection with *ergodic theory*. This is the map

$$\tau(x, y) = \left(\frac{1}{x} - a_1, \frac{1}{a_1 + y}\right)$$

where the number x has the continued fraction expansion $[0; a_1, a_2, a_3, ...]$. Note that the second component balances the loss of information, namely the first digit a_1 in the first component. We call the number

$$t_n = \cfrac{1}{a_{n+1} + \cfrac{1}{a_{n+2} + ...}}$$

the *future* of x at time n and the number

$$v_n = \cfrac{1}{a_n + ...\cfrac{1}{a_1}}$$

its *past* at time n. Note that

$$v_n = \frac{q_{n-1}}{q_n}, \; t_{n+1} = \frac{1}{t_n} - a_{n+1}, \; v_{n+1} = \frac{1}{a_{n+1} + v_n}.$$

A calculation shows

$$D_{n-2} = \frac{(a_n + t_n)v_n}{1 - a_n v_n}, \; D_{n-1} = \frac{1}{t_n v_n}, \; D_n = \frac{(a_{n+1} + v_n)t_n}{1 - a_{n+1} t_n}.$$

Put $a_n = a$ and $a_{n+1} = b$. We define for real numbers $r, R > 1$ the functions

$$f_{a,r}(t) = \frac{r}{a(r+1) + t}$$

and

$$g_{b,R}(t) = \frac{R}{t} - b(R+1).$$

Then $D_{n-2} < r$ is equivalent to $v_n < f_{a,r}(t_n)$ and $D_n < R$ to $v_n < g_{b,R}(t_n)$. [Kraaikamp & Smeets 2011] continued previous work of Jing Chen Tong (see e. g. [Tong 1991]). By elementary but tedious calculations they obtained sharp bounds of the following kind. If $D_{n-2} < r$ and $D_n < R$ then they obtained the exact lower bound for D_{n-1}, Here the the number

$$2M = \frac{1}{r} + \frac{1}{R} + ab(1 + \frac{1}{r})(1 + \frac{1}{R}) + \sqrt{\left(\frac{1}{r} + \frac{1}{R} + ab(1 + \frac{1}{r})(1 + \frac{1}{R})\right)^2 - \frac{4}{rR}}$$

enters which is connected with the intersection point of the curves given by $f_{a,r}$ and $g_{b,R}$ plays an essential role. In a similar way the case $D_{n-2} > r$ and $D_n > R$ is treated.

As can be guessed from these examples continued fractions are a major tool in *Diophantine approximations* (see [Koksma 1936], [Cassels 1957], [Lang 1966], [Sprindžuk 1979], [Harman 1998], [Bugeaud 2012]). In fact continued fractions provide *best approximations*. If $\frac{p_n}{q_n}$ is the n-th convergent to α and the denominator of a rational number $\frac{a}{b}$ satisfies $0 < b < q_n$ then the inequality

$$|\alpha b - a| > |\alpha q_n - p_n|$$

holds. Obviously the Dutch mathematician and astronomer Christian Huygens detected this wonderful property when he built his automatic planetarium (see [Brezinski 1991] for a good account of Huygens results).

A classical result is attributed to [Lejeune Dirichlet 1842]. The proof uses the so-called *pigeon-hole principle*. If you have $Q + 1$ birds in Q cages then there exists a cage with at least two birds in it. Let $x \in [0, 1[$ and $Q > 1$ an integer. Then there is a pair of integers p and q such that $0 < q < Q$ and

$$|qx - p| \leq \frac{1}{Q}.$$

One considers first the sequence $x, 2x, ..., (Q - 1)x$ and then the the $Q + 1$ points $0, x - n_1, 2x - n_2, ..., (Q - 1)x - n_{Q-1}, 1$ where the natural numbers n_j are chosen such that $0 \leq jx - n_j < 1$. The interval $[0, 1]$ will be divided into Q intervals $[\frac{i}{Q}, \frac{i+1}{Q}[$, $i = 0, 1, ..., Q - 2$ and $[\frac{Q-1}{Q}, 1]$. Then there must be at least one interval $[\frac{i}{Q}, \frac{i+1}{Q}[$ (or $[\frac{Q-1}{Q}, 1]$) which contains two points. This means that for some r, s with $r < s < Q$ the inequality

$$|(sx - n_s) - (rx - n_r)| \leq \frac{1}{Q}$$

or the inequality

$$|sx - n_s - 1| \leq \frac{1}{Q}$$

holds. Then we choose $p = n_s - n_r$ and $q = s - r$ (or $p = n_s - 1$ and $q = s$). This theorem can also be used as a stating point for continued fractions (see [Cassels 1957]).

We further mention Chebyshev's theorem. For arbitrary α and β the inequality

$$|\alpha x - y - \beta| < \frac{3}{x}$$

has infinitely many solutions in integers x and y. It turns out that the quality of approximation of the linear inhomogeneous form $\alpha x - y - \beta$ is in some sense dual to the quality of approximation for the linear homogeneous problem $\alpha x - y$ (see e. g. [Koksma 1936] and [Cassels 1957]). These problems are connected with the growth of the partial denominators a_n of the continued fraction for α.

A finite continued fraction represents an rational number. It is also easy to prove the other direction. Let $x = \frac{a}{b}$ be a rational number, $0 < x < 1$, in its lowest terms. Then $Tx = \frac{b}{a} - k = \frac{b - ak}{a}$ has a smaller denominator. Hence after finitely many steps the algorithm must stop. The continued fraction algorithm is equivalent with Euclid's algorithm for finding the greatest common divisor of the integers a and b.

If $0 < x = \frac{a}{b} < 1$ is a given rational number with its expansion

$$\frac{a}{b} = \cfrac{1}{a_1 + \cfrac{1}{a_2 + ... + \cfrac{1}{a_n}}}$$

one can estimate the length $n = N(a, b)$. An old result is due to [Lamé 1844]. He proved that $N(a, b) < 5k$ where k denotes the number of decimal digits of b. Since

$$q_n = a_n q_{n-1} + q_{n-2} \geq q_{n-1} + q_{n-2}$$

we find $q_n \geq G^{n-1}$ where G is the number of the Golden Section, $G = \frac{1+\sqrt{5}}{2}$. Since $\frac{a}{b} = \frac{p_n}{q_n}$ and $b = q_n$ (here we assume that the fraction is given in its reduced form) we find a similar estimate

$$n = N(a, b) \leq \frac{\log b}{\log G} + 1.$$

[Heilbronn 1969] gave the remarkable result

$$\sum_{1 \leq a < b,\, (a,b)=1} N(a, b) = \frac{12 \log 2}{\pi^2} \varphi(b) \log b + O\big(b \log^3 \log b\big).$$

Here $\varphi(b)$ is the number of a, $1 \leq a < b$ with the greatest common divisor $(a, b) = 1$, the *Euler function* (see also [Dixon 1970]). This result was refined by other authors ([Porter 1975], [Tonkov 1974/75]) and could be generalized to other algorithms like the algorithm to the nearest integer or singular continued fractions ([Rieger 1978]).

A famous theorem of Lagrange says that a continued fraction of a number x is *periodic* if and only if x is a quadratic irrational number. Periodicity means that after the first elements $a_0, a_1, ..., a_m$ the next elements $a_{m+1}, a_{m+2}, ..., a_{m+n}$ are repeated periodically. If $0 < x < 1$ then this equivalent to $T^{n+m}x = T^n x$. One direction is very easy. It is clear that we can concentrate on purely periodic expansions, i. e. no preperiod. Then $T^n x = x$ and the equation

$$x = \frac{p_n + p_{n-1}x}{q_n + q_{n-1}x}$$

immediately gives a quadratic equation for x. If x were a rational number its continued fraction expansion would be finite. Therefore x is an irrational number. The real problem is the opposite assertion. If x is a quadratic irrational number then its continued fraction expansion would eventually become

periodic. [Perron 1954] gives several proofs and refers to the history of the
problem.

This question is much more delicate for generalizations of regular continued
fractions. [Oppenheim 1960] following [Bankier & Leighton 1942] calls a continued fraction of the form

$$b_0 + \cfrac{a_1}{b_1 + \cfrac{a_2}{b_2 + \cfrac{a_3}{b_3 + ...}}}$$

proper if the integers a_i, b_i satisfy the inequalities $1 \le a_i \le b_i$. He proves that
every quadratic irrational admits of infinitely many periodic proper continued
fraction representations. Indeed, only one term is needed in the periodic part
and at most three terms in the non-periodic part!

There are interesting results concerning periodicity for some variations of the
regular continued fraction algorithm (for latest results see e. g. [Dajani &
Kraaikamp & van der Wekken 2013] and [Dajani & Kraaikamp & Langeveld
2015]). We further mention Ryde's *continued fraction with non-decreasing
digits*. He proved in [Ryde 1951] that there exist quadratic irrational numbers
for which the algorithm is not ultimately periodic (for a similar expansion see
[Hartono & Kraaikamp & Schweiger 2002]). Since his method is connected
with *Pell equations* it should be mentioned that regular continued fractions
provide solutions of equations of the form

$$x^2 - Dy^2 = 1,$$

where $D \ge 1$ and D is not a square. This equation has infinitely many integer
solutions (x, y). If (x, y) and $(\overline{x}, \overline{y})$ are solutions, then the pair $(x\overline{x} + Dy\overline{y}, x\overline{y} + \overline{x}y)$ is also a solution. This was already known in classical Indian mathematics.
If one considers the continued fraction of $\sqrt{D}$ then the sequence (p_n, q_n) con-
tains a solution. Information on the Pell equation and its connection to units
in quadratic number fields can be found in many books on number theory.

Chapter 3

Expansions into a series

If $p \geq 2$ is an integer the representation

$$x = \sum_{n=1}^{\infty} \frac{\varepsilon_n}{p^n}$$

for a real number $0 \leq x < 1$ is well known and we will refer to it very often. For practical purposes the case $p = 10$ is the most common base. In computer science the base $p = 2$ has some importance. But the base $p = 16$ is also of some interest (hexadecimal expansion). In this case one has to introduce new digits $A = 10, B = 11, C = 12, D = 13, E = 14$, and $F = 15$. Then one calculates e.g.

$$0.859375 = \frac{D}{10} + \frac{C}{10^2}.$$

Note that in hexadecimal notation $10 = 16$ and $10^2 = 16 \cdot 16$ where on the right hand side we use decimal notation.

However, there are many other modes to represent a number as an (infinite) series. Since in most cases these expansions do not arise as f-expansions we just give them passing notice. A classical account is [Perron 1960]. With some reservations we mention [Galambos 1976]. A very recent account is [Berthé 2012].

We first follow Perron's book to present some of the classical series. The first will be *Cantor series*. Let $p_1, p_2, p_3, \ldots$ be a fixed sequence of integers, $p_j \geq 2, j = 1, 2, 3, \ldots$. If $0 \leq \gamma_0 < 1$ we define

$$c_1 = \lfloor \gamma_0 p_1 \rfloor, \ \gamma_1 = \gamma_0 p_1 - c_1$$

13

$$c_2 = \lfloor \gamma_1 p_2 \rfloor, \ \gamma_2 = \gamma_1 p_2 - c_2$$

...

This leads to the series

$$\gamma_0 = \frac{c_1}{p_1} + \frac{c_2}{p_1 p_2} + \frac{c_3}{p_1 p_2 p_3} + \dots.$$

which goes back to [Cantor 1869a]. It is easy to show that every series of the form

$$\sum_{n=1}^{\infty} \frac{c_n}{p_1 p_2 \dots p_n}, \ 0 \le c_n < p_n$$

with the condition that $c_n \le p_n - 2$ infinitely many often is the unique Cantor series of a real number γ_0, $0 \le \gamma_o < 1$. The condition $c_n \le p_n - 2$ infinitely many often is the generalization of avoiding the ambiguity $1 = \sum_{n=1}^{\infty} \frac{9}{10^n}$. Perron gives an interesting result. Let $p_1, p_2, p_3, \dots$ be a sequence such that every prime number divides infinitely many numbers p_n. Then γ_0 is rational if there is an N such that $c_n = 0$ for all $n \ge N + 1$.

The proof runs as follows. Let $\gamma_0 = \frac{a}{b}$ be a rational number then

$$\gamma_0 = \frac{a}{b} = \sum_{k=1}^{n} \frac{c_k}{p_1 p_2 \dots p_n} + \frac{\gamma_{n+1}}{p_1 p_2 \dots p_{n+1}}$$

and

$$\gamma_0 p_1 p_2 \dots p_n = \sum_{k=1}^{n} c_k p_{k+1} \dots p_n + c_n + \frac{\gamma_{n+1}}{p_{n+1}}.$$

If the number n is chosen big enough b divides the product $p_1 p_2 \dots p_n$. Then we see $\gamma_{n+1} = 0$ and $\gamma_k = 0$ for all $k \ge n + 1$.

If one applies this result to $p_n = n + 1$ we find that

$$e - 2 = \sum_{n=1}^{\infty} \frac{1}{(n + 1)!}$$

is not a rational number.

Perron introduces the series expansions named after Lüroth, Engel, and Sylvester in a uniform way which we simplify to some extent.

Let $0 < x_0 = x \le 1$ and let $r_1, r_2, r_3, \dots$ be a sequence of positive integers. Then we define $q_1 \ge 2$ by the equation

$$q_1 - 1 \le \frac{1}{x_0} < q_1.$$

This can be rewritten as

$$\frac{1}{q_1} < x_0 \leq \frac{1}{q_1 - 1} = \frac{1}{q_1} + \frac{1}{(q_1 - 1)q_1}.$$

Then there is a unique number x_1 such that

$$x_0 = \frac{1}{q_1} + \frac{r_1}{(q_1 - 1)q_1}x_1$$

with $r_1 x_1 \leq 1$. If we iterate this process we obtain an expansion

$$x = \frac{1}{q_1} + \frac{r_1}{(q_1 - 1)q_1 q_2} + \frac{r_1 r_2}{(q_1 - 1)q_1(q_2 - 1)q_2 q_3} + ... + \frac{r_1 ... r_n}{(q_1 - 1)q_1 ... (q_n - 1)q_n}x_n.$$

Since $r_k x_k \leq 1$, $1 \leq k \leq n$ and $q_{k+1} - 1 \leq \frac{1}{x_k} < q_{k+1}$ we obtain $r_k \leq q_{k+1} - 1$.
Therefore

$$\frac{r_1 ... r_k}{(q_1 - 1)q_1 ... (q_k - 1)q_k} \leq \frac{q_{k+1} - 1}{(q_1 - 1)q_1 q_2 ... q_k}.$$

Then

$$\frac{1}{q_1} + \sum_{k=1}^{n-1} \frac{r_1 ... r_k}{(q_1 - 1)q_1 ... (q_k - 1)q_k q_{k+1}}$$

$$\leq \frac{1}{q_1 - 1}\left(1 - \frac{1}{q_1} + \sum_{k=1}^{n-1}(\frac{1}{q_1 q_2 ... q_k} - \frac{1}{q_1 q_2 ... q_{k+1}})\right)$$

$$= \frac{1}{q_1 - 1}\left(1 - \frac{1}{q_1 q_2 ... q_n}\right) < \frac{1}{q_1 - 1}.$$

This shows that all these series are convergent. Conversely, if we choose
$q_{k+1} \geq r_k + 1$ then we have convergence.
If $r_k \equiv 1$ then we have the *Lüroth series* which was published in [Lüroth 1883].
In this case $q_k \geq 2$ is the only condition.
If $r_k = q_k - 1$ we have the condition $q_{k+1} \geq q_k \geq 2$. This expansion is called
Engel series since Perron refers to a paper by Engel in *Verhandlungen der 52.*
Versammlung deutscher Philologen und Schulmänner in Marburg 1913. In fact
W. Sierpiński published a paper in Polish which contains the same algorithm
[Sierpiński 1911]. The paper was later translated into French and appeared in
his selected works [Sierpiński 1974]. We will shortly come back to it.
If $r_k = (q_k - 1)q_k$ then the expansion is named *Sylvester series* with the growth
condition $q_{k+1} \geq (q_k - 1)q_k + 1$. It is named after [Sylvester 1881]. These series
are related to *Egyptian fractions*, the study of representations of the form

$$x = \frac{1}{a_1} + \frac{1}{a_2} + \frac{1}{a_3} + ...$$

(see e. g. [Bleicher & Erdös 1976a, 1976b]).
Perron gives an interesting example. Define

$$t_{k+1} = 2t_k^2 - 1$$

with a start value $t_0 \geq 2$. Then

$$\sqrt{t_{k+1}^2 - 1} = 2t_k \sqrt{t_k^2 - 1}$$

and

$$t_0 - \sqrt{t_0^2 - 1} = \frac{1}{2t_0} + \frac{t_1 - \sqrt{t_1^2 - 1}}{2t_0}.$$

Therefore

$$t_0 - \sqrt{t_0^2 - 1} = \sum_{k=1}^{\infty} \frac{1}{2t_0 \cdot 2t_1 \cdot \ldots \cdot 2t_{k-1}}$$

which is an Egyptian fraction. This result goes back [Stratemeyer 1931].

Since Sierpiński's paper „O kilku algorytmach dla rozwijania liczb rzeczywistych na szeregi" went unnoticed through many years it is appropriate to
report shortly on its content. The starting point of the first part is a real
number x_0 and the following algorithm

$$\frac{1}{x_{k-1}} = a_k + b_k \text{ with } a_k \geq 1, \ 0 < b_k < 1, \ k \geq 1.$$

This gives an expansion

$$x_0 = \frac{1}{a_1} - \frac{1}{a_2} + \frac{1}{a_3} - \ldots + (-1)^{n-1} \frac{1}{a_n} + (-1)^n x_n.$$

Later he restricts to the case where the numbers $a_1, a_2, \ldots$ are integers $a_{n+1} = \lfloor \frac{1}{x_n} \rfloor$. Sierpiński uses the notation $E \frac{1}{x_n}$ obviously for the French word *entier*
(= integer). If x_0 is irrational then

$$\frac{1}{x_n} - 1 < a_{n+1} < \frac{1}{x_n}.$$

Therefore we find

$$0 < \frac{1}{x_n} - a_{n+1} < 1$$

and $a_{n+1} \geq a_n(a_n + 1)$. If x_0 is rational the algorithm terminates. An example
is

$$\frac{169}{408} = \frac{1}{2} - \frac{1}{11} + \frac{1}{195} - \frac{1}{291720}.$$

Sierpiński mentions an older paper with similar results [Cohen 1891]. Today we would call it a Sylvester series with alternating signs.
Next he considers expansions of the form

$$x_0 = \frac{1}{a_1} - \frac{1}{a_1 a_2} + \frac{1}{a_1 a_2 a_3} - ..., \, a_j \geq 1 \, \text{integers}.$$

Since this means $x_n = 1 - a_n x_{n-1}$ this expansion is Pierce's algorithm ([Pierce 1929]).
He mentions that this algorithm shows that

$$\frac{e-1}{e} = \frac{1}{1} - \frac{1}{1 \cdot 2} + \frac{1}{1 \cdot 2 \cdot 3} - \frac{1}{1 \cdot 2 \cdot 3 \cdot 4} + ...$$

is irrational.
Next he goes to

$$x_0 = \frac{1}{a_1} + \frac{1}{a_1 a_2} + \frac{1}{a_1 a_2 a_3} + ...$$

where $a_{n+1} \geq a_n$ which is Engel's series. Out of many examples we mention the series

$$\frac{a - \sqrt{a^2 - 4}}{2} = \frac{1}{a_1} + \frac{1}{a_1 a_2} + \frac{1}{a_1 a_2 a_3} + ...$$

where $a_1 = a$ and $a_{n+1} = a_n^2 - 2$. For $a = 3$ this series was already obtained by E. Lucas in [Lucas 1891].
In this paper there are some more series expansions and some interesting references to older literature which we do not expose here.

The metrical theory of Lüroth series was developed in the frame work of *ergodic theory* in [Jager & De Vroedt 1969]. The underlying map is defined as

$$Tx = k(k+1)x - k, \, k = \lfloor \frac{1}{x} \rfloor.$$

This map preserves Lebesgue measure and is ergodic on the unit interval. A first example of a *jump transformation* is given at the end of the paper. If

$$x = \sum_{j=1}^{\infty} \frac{\varepsilon_j(x)}{2^j}$$

then define

$$Sx = \sum_{j=N}^{\infty} \frac{\varepsilon_j(x)}{2^j}$$

if $\varepsilon_1(x) = \ldots = \varepsilon_{N-1}(x) = 0$, but $\varepsilon_N(x) = 1$.

Berg continues in his papers [Berg 1955, 1957, 1958] investigations from [Holzer 1928]. Similar to Lehmer's approach [Lehmer 1938] he investigates the iteration of functions $f(a, \xi)$ but very often he is concerned with the special case

$$f(a, \xi) = f_0(a) + f_1(a)\xi, \ a \in \mathbb{Z}, \ \xi \in [0, 1]$$

which includes the series expansions of Lüroth, Engel and Sylvester. Here f_0 and f_1 denote functions defined on the natural numbers. However, his conditions are a little bit complicated and he does not use the underlying maps $T : [0, 1] \to [0, 1]$. Let x be a real number which satisfies $0 < x \le 1$ then the sequence of numbers (a_n) and (x_n) are defined as

$$x_0 = x, \ f(a_n, 0) < x_{n-1} \le f(a_n - 1, 0), \ x_{n-1} = f(a_n, x_n).$$

The residues x_n satisfy the condition $0 < x_n \le \eta_n$, the numbers a_n the growth condition $a_n \ge a_n^*$ for some number a_n^*. If one uses the language of fibred systems then the underlying map $T : [0, 1] \to [0, 1]$ maps the interval $]f(a_n, 0), f(a_n - 1, 0)]$ onto $]0, \eta_n]$. Since η_n can be smaller than 1 a restriction $a_n \ge a_n^*$ can occur.

In [Berg 1955] sets with the following property are considered. If $x \in M$ then $x_n \in M$ for all $n \ge 0$. This is not exactly ergodicity because $TM \subseteq M$ does not imply $T^{-1}M = M$ but ergodicity is a sufficient condition. The main theorem is the following. If $\eta_n = 1$ for all $n \ge 1$ then every set M is *homogeneous* in $[0, 1]$, i. e. its density is constant and therefore $\lambda(M) = 0$ or $\lambda(M) = 1$ (see the chapter *Measure zero or one*). For the Engel series which corresponds to $f(a, \xi) = \frac{1+\xi}{a}$ this condition is not satisfied since $\eta_n = \frac{1}{a_n - 1}$ but Berg shows that if $x \in M$ additionally implies $\frac{1+\xi}{a} \in M$ then M is homogeneous. The main part of the paper deals with complicated calculations of the measure of the set E_k of all points x which satisfy the equation $a_n(x) = a_n^* + k$, $k \ge 0$ fixed, only finitely many often.

The papers [Berg 1957] and [Berg 1958] continue these investigations. Interesting is the following example. Let $\varepsilon > 1$ and $f(a, \xi) = \varepsilon^{-a+1} + (1 - \varepsilon^{-1})\xi$. For sake of simplicity we present the underlying fibred system.

$$Tx = \frac{\varepsilon x - \varepsilon^{-a+2}}{\varepsilon - 1}, \ \varepsilon^{-a+1} < x \le \varepsilon^{-a+2}, \ a \ge 2.$$

Note that the points ε^{-a+2} are fixed points. Then $\lambda(E_k) = 0$. Remember that for Engel series one has $\lambda(E_k) = 1$. In [Berg 1958] the construction of the function $f(a, \xi)$ is changed in a way to ensure that certain sets M are not homogeneous.

Out from further results on Engel and Sylvester series we mention that in [Erdös & Rényi & Szüsz 1958] the main focus is as follows. If

$$x = \frac{1}{q_1} + \frac{1}{q_1 q_2} + \frac{1}{q_1 q_2 q_3} + ...$$

is an Engel series then the distribution of the random variables

$$x_n = \log \frac{q_n}{q_{n-1}}, \; q_0 = 1, \; q_n \geq 2 \, \text{for } n \geq 1$$

is studied, e. g.

$$\frac{\log q_n - n}{\sqrt{n}}$$

tends to the normal distribution. If

$$x = \frac{1}{Q_1} + \frac{1}{Q_2} + \frac{1}{Q_3} + ...$$

is a Sylvester series then the two random variables

$$X_n = \log \frac{Q_n}{Q_n^2}, \; Q_0 = 1, \; Y_n = \log \frac{Q_n}{Q_1 Q_2 ... Q_{n-1}}$$

are considered. A special approach to Engel series is outlined in [Rényi 1962]. If the random variable $\varepsilon_k(x)$ counts how many times k occurs in the sequence $q_n(x)$, $n \geq 1$ then the random variables $\varepsilon_k(x)$ are independent and their distribution is given as

$$P(\varepsilon_k = r) = \frac{k-1}{k^{r+1}}.$$

One corollary is mentioned. For almost all points x the sequence $q_n(x)$ is strictly increasing for $n \geq n_0(x)$.

A comprehensive study of series expansions is [Vervaat 1992]. He generalizes the so-called *Balkema-Oppenheim expansions*. These expansions were studied in [Oppenheim 1971] and in [Balkema 1968]. The paper [Oppenheim 1971] is devoted to the study of six series. We mention two examples

$$\sum \frac{1}{2d_i + 1}$$

and

$$\sum \frac{\varepsilon_1 \varepsilon_2 ... \varepsilon_{i-1}}{(2d_1 + 1)(2d_2 + 1)...(2d_i + 1)}$$

where the ε_j take the values $+1$ or -1. In some sense the expansions considered in [Berg 1955] are more general. [Galambos 1976] gives many interesting results but the text is impaired by several errors.

Let (α_n), $n \geq 1$ be a strictly decreasing sequence of real numbers with $\alpha(1) = 1$ and $\lim_{n\to\infty} \alpha_n = 0$. Let the function $d :]0, 1] \to \mathbb{N}$ defined as

$$d(x) = n, \ \alpha(n) < x \leq \alpha(n-1), \ n \geq 2$$

which means

$$\alpha(d(x)) = \sup\{\alpha(n) : \alpha(n) < x\}.$$

Let further be given a map $h : \mathbb{N} \setminus \{1\} \to \mathbb{N}$. Since

$$0 < x - \alpha(d(x)) \leq \alpha(d(x) - 1) - \alpha(d(x))$$

we obtain

$$0 < \frac{x - \alpha(d(x))}{\alpha(d(x) - 1) - \alpha(d(x))} \leq 1.$$

The interval $]\alpha(n), \alpha(n-1)]$ which contains $x_1 = x$ is mapped linearly onto $]0, \alpha(h(n))]$ and we define

$$x_2 = \frac{x - \alpha(d(x))}{\alpha(d(x) - 1) - \alpha(d(x))} \alpha(h(d(x))).$$

Since $0 < x_2 \leq 1$ one can repeat this procedure. If we put

$$\gamma(k) = \frac{\alpha(k-1) - \alpha(k))}{\alpha(h(k))}$$

for $k \geq 2$ and $d_k = d(x_k) = d(x_k)$ for $k \geq 1$ we see that

$$x_n = \alpha(d_n) + \gamma(d_n) x_{n+1}.$$

Iteration gives the formal series

$$x = \sum_{n=1}^{\infty} \alpha(d_n) \prod_{k=1}^{n-1} \gamma(d_k).$$

Since

$$\sum_{n=1}^{N} \alpha(d_n) \prod_{k=1}^{n-1} \gamma(d_k) \leq x$$

the convergence is clear but not the identification of the limit. Vervaat calls a sequence (j_n) *realizable* (with respect to h) if $j_1 \geq 2$ and $j_{k+1} \geq h(j_k) + 1$. He says that the Balkema-Oppenheim expansion is *separating* if the formal series is convergent to limit x. In fact there are non-separating expansions. He gives the example

$$\alpha(n) = e^{-\frac{1}{2}n(n-1)}, \; h(n) = n.$$

Then $\gamma(n) = e^{n-1} - 1$ and the sequence $j_n = n + 1$ is realizable. The length of the interval

$$I(j_1, ..., j_n) = \{x : d(x_1) = j_1, ..., d(x_n) = j_n\}$$

is given as

$$\gamma(d_1)...\gamma(d_{n-1}(\alpha(j_n - 1) - \alpha(j_n)) = (1 - e^{-1})...(1 - e^{-n+1}(1 - e^{-n}).$$

This product converges to a positive number. Therefore $\bigcap_n I(j_1, ..., j_n)$ contains infinitely many numbers which have the same expansion.

Vervaat presents a long list of special cases. We mention just a few.

- Lüroth series: $h(n) = 1$, $\alpha(n) = \frac{1}{n}$, $\gamma(n) = \frac{1}{n(n-1)}$

- Engel series: $h(n) = n - 1$, $\alpha(n) = \frac{1}{n}$, $\gamma(n) = \frac{1}{n}$

- Modified Engel series ([Rényi 1962]): $h(n) = n$, $\alpha(n) = \frac{1}{n}$, $\gamma(n) = \frac{1}{n-1}$

- Sylvester series: $h(n) = n(n - 1)$, $\alpha(n) = \frac{1}{n}$, $\gamma(n) = 1$

- Cantor product: $h(n) = n^2 - 1$, $\alpha(n) = \frac{\log(1+n)}{\log 2}$, $\gamma(n) = 1$ In this case we get

$$x \log 2 = \log(1 + \frac{1}{d_1}) + \log(1 + \frac{1}{d_2}) + \log(1 + \frac{1}{d_3}) + ...$$

$$2^x = (1 + \frac{1}{d_1})(1 + \frac{1}{d_1})(1 + \frac{1}{d_1}) \cdots .$$

If we put $\alpha = 2^x$ this is the Cantor product as defined for $\alpha > 1$ in [Perron 1960].

Vervaat's main interest lies in the study of the digits $d_k(x)$, $k = 1, 2, 3, ...$ which form a *stationary Markoff chain*. Its initial distribution is

$$P(d_1(x) = j) = \alpha(j - 1) - \alpha(j), \; j \geq 2$$

$$P(d_{n+1}(x) = k | d_n(x) = j) = \frac{\alpha(k - 1) - \alpha(k)}{\alpha(h(j))}, \; k, j \geq 2, \; k > h(j)$$

and

$$P(d_{n+1}(x) = k | d_n(x) = j) = 0$$

else.

The most interesting result is that the map

$$Tx = x - \frac{1}{d}, \frac{1}{d} < x \le \frac{1}{d-1}, d \ge 2$$

related to Sylvester series is not *ergodic* which means there exist *invariant sets* E with $0 < \lambda(E) < 1$ (see also [Goldie & Smith 1987]). A set E is called invariant if $T^{-1}E = E$.

From many other papers on various series expansions we mention [Kalpazidou & Knopfmacher & Knopfmacher 1990, 1991]. The modification of Lüroth series is quite obvious. Define

$$a_1(x) = \lfloor \frac{1}{x} \rfloor, Tx = (a_1(x) + 1)(1 - a_1(x)x), a_{n+1}(x) = a_1(T^n x).$$

Then we get the finite or infinite series

$$x = \frac{1}{a_1} + \sum_{n \ge 2} \frac{(-1)^{n-1}}{a_1(a_1 + 1)...a_{n-1}(a_{n-1} + 1)a_n}.$$

Since T is *ergodic* and the Lebesgue measure λ is *invariant* theorems about the frequency of digits and similar points follow by standard methods.

Chapter 4

Infinite products

In [Perron 1960] the classical case of *Cantor products* is considered. If $\alpha \geq 1$ then there is a unique representation of the form

$$\alpha_0 = \prod_{j=0}^{\infty} (1 + \frac{1}{q_j})$$

if $q_j \geq 1$ are integers, $q_{j+1} \geq q_j^2$, and $q_j \geq 2$ for $j \geq j(\alpha_0)$ [Cantor 1869b].
Perron mentions the following result: Let $q_0 = q > 1$, $q_{j+1} = 2q_j^2 - 1$, then

$$\sqrt{\frac{q+1}{q-1}} = \prod_{j=0}^{\infty} (1 + \frac{1}{q_j}).$$

He calls this result „Formel von Engel". Clearly, infinite products have been very common since the early days of differential calculus. We mention the famous product of John Wallis

$$\frac{\pi}{2} = \frac{2^2 \cdot 4^2 \cdot 6^2 \cdot \dots}{3^2 \cdot 5^2 \cdot 7^2 \cdot \dots}.$$

We mention that [Lacroix 1993] discusses infinite products as fibred systems. This can be illustrated with Cantor products. Take $B = [1, 2]$ and the partition $B(k) =]\frac{k+1}{k}, \frac{k}{k-1}]$, $k = 2, 3, \dots$ The map T is given as

$$Tx = \frac{k_1 x}{k_1 + 1} \text{ for } x \in B(k_1).$$

23

Then $TB(k) =]1, \frac{k_1^2}{k_1^2-1}]$. Therefore the next digit satifies $k_2 \geq k_1^2$.
[Oppenheim 1953] considers products of the form

$$x = \prod_{j=1}^{\infty}(1 + \frac{n_j}{d_j})$$

where the integers $n_j \geq 1$ are given and the numbers $d_j = d_j(x)$ depend on the given number x. This leads to remarkable expansions for quadratic irrationals, e. g.

$$\sqrt{2} = (1 + \frac{2}{5})(1 + \frac{2}{197})(1 + \frac{2}{7761797})....$$

which is attributed to [Escott 1937].

A comparison between different series expansions and the Cantor product leads to the issue of a representation of the form

$$x = \prod_{j=1}^{\infty}(1 + \frac{1}{a_1 a_2 ... a_j}), \; a_{j+1} \geq a_j, \text{starting with } a_1 \geq 1.$$

Strange enough a first attempt does not lead to a really satisfactory result [Knopfmacher & Knopfmacher 1987]. Let $x > 1$ and put $x = 2^k x_1, 1 < x_1 \leq 2$. Then define

$$a_n = 1 + \lfloor \frac{1}{x_n - 1} \rfloor, \; x_n \neq 1$$

$$x_{n+1} = \frac{a_1 a_2 ... a_n}{a_1 a_2 ... a_n + 1} x_n.$$

The definition of x_{n+1} implies

$$1 < x_{n+1} < x_n.$$

Therefore $a_{n+1} \geq a_n$. We define

$$\lambda(x) = \lim_{n \to \infty} x_n$$

and using

$$x_1 = (1 + \frac{1}{a_1})(1 + \frac{1}{a_1 a_2})...(1 + \frac{1}{a_1 a_2 ... a_n}) x_{n+1}$$

we obtain

$$x = 2^k \lambda(x) \prod_{j=1}^{\infty}(1 + \frac{1}{a_1 a_2 ... a_j}).$$

The definition of a_n is equivalent to

$$1 + \frac{1}{a_n} < x_n \le 1 + \frac{1}{a_n - 1}.$$

If $a_m = a$ for all $m \ge m_0$ then we obtain

$$1 + \frac{1}{a} \le \lambda(x) < 1 + \frac{1}{a - 1}.$$

Note that the sequence x_n is strictly decreasing. If $\lambda(x) > 1$ then

$$a_n \le 1 + \frac{1}{x_n - 1} < 1 + \frac{1}{\lambda(x) - 1}.$$

Since the sequence a_n is increasing one sees that $a_m = a$ for $m \ge m_0$. The authors also mention that for $A = 1 + \frac{1}{a-1}$, $a \ge 3$ one finds $a_1 = a$, $a_2 = a^2$, $a_3 = a^2 + a$, $a_i = a^2 + a + 1$ for $i \ge 4$. In this case $1 + \frac{1}{a^2+a+1} < \lambda(A)$.

Therefore a new algorithm is proposed. Let $x > 1$, $x = 2^k x_1$, $1 < x_1 \le 2$ as before. Then define

$$a_n = 1 + \lfloor \frac{1}{a_1 a_2 ... a_{n-1}(x_n - 1)} \rfloor, \; x_n \ne 1, \; x_{n+1} = \frac{a_1 a_2 ... a_n}{a_1 a_2 ... a_n + 1} x_n.$$

As before we have the conditions $1 < x_{n+1} < x_n$ and $2 \le a_n \le a_{n+1}$. Since

$$x_n \le 1 + \frac{1}{a_1 a_2 ... a_{n-1}(a_n - 1)}$$

we obtain $\lim_{n \to \infty} x_n = 1$.
This shows that

$$x = 2^k \prod_{j=1}^{\infty} (1 + \frac{1}{a_1 a_2 ... a_j})$$

where $a_1 \ge 2$, $a_{j+1} \ge a_j$, for all $j \ge 1$. This representation can be converted to the form

$$x = \prod_{j=1}^{\infty} (1 + \frac{1}{a_1 a_2 ... a_j})$$

where $a_1 = a_2 = ... = a_k = 1$, $a_{k+1} \ge 2$. Unfortunately, this product representation is not unique.
The key to it is the old formula of Euler

$$\prod_{j=0}^{\infty} (1 + x^{2^j}) = \frac{1}{1 - x}, \quad \text{for } |x| < 1.$$

If we use the notation

$$(a_1, a_2, a_3, \ldots) = \prod_{j=1}^{\infty} (1 + \frac{1}{a_1 a_2 \ldots a_j})$$

then one obtains

$$\frac{15}{7} = \frac{8}{7}(1 + \frac{1}{2})(1 + \frac{1}{4}) = (2, 2, 2, 8, 8^2, 8^4, \ldots)$$

$$\frac{15}{7} = 2(1 + \frac{1}{14}) = (1, 15, 15, 15^2, 15^4, \ldots).$$

Chapter 5

Kakeya's attempt

[Kakeya 1924] is probably the first paper which tried to unify decimal fractions and continued fractions. In his paper he considers functions

$$f : [0, 1] \rightarrow \mathbb{R}$$

with the properties

(1) f is continuous and monotonic

(2) If $f(0) = \alpha$, $f(1) = \beta$ the numbers α and β are integers

(3) f is differentiable almost everywhere and $|f'(x)| > 1$ almost everywhere.

If $\alpha < \beta$ then Kakeya speaks of case A. If $\beta < \alpha$ then he speaks of case B. Let $\omega \in \mathbb{R}$ he then introduces two sequences

$$a_1 := \lfloor \omega \rfloor, \omega_1 := \omega - a_1$$
$$a_n := \lfloor f(\omega_{n-1}) \rfloor, \omega_n := f(\omega_{n-1}) - a_n, n \geq z.$$

In case A the sequence (a_n) is called *of the first kind* if $\alpha \leq a_n < \beta$ for $n \geq 2$. In case B the sequence (a_n) is called *of the first kind* if $\beta \leq a_n < \alpha$ for $n \geq z$. The sequence of integers $(a_1, a_2, a_3, \ldots)$, thus obtained, is called the *notation* of ω with respect to the *scale function* f. This sequence $(a_1, a_2, a_3, \ldots)$ is nowadays known as the *sequence of digits* of ω.
The equations

$$\omega = a_1 + \omega_1, f(\omega_1) = a_2 + \omega_2 \ldots, f(\omega_{n-1}) = a_n + \omega_n, \ldots$$

eventually lead to the expression

$$\omega = a_1 + g(a_2 + g(a_3 + \cdots + g(a_n + \omega_n)\ldots))$$

and if $n \to \infty$ to the formal expression

$$\omega = a_1 + g(a_2 + g(a_3 + \cdots + g(a_n + \ldots))).$$

Here g denotes the inverse function of f. This is exactly an *f-expansion*. Kakeya calls it a *functional continuation*. Two remarks are in order: Kakeya's case A later is called type B and Kakeya's case B became type A. Furthermore, in later papers as we will see the function g is denoted as f and Kakeya's f as f^{-1}. Very puzzling!

The next step is to introduce the sequence of functions

$$S_n(x) = a_1 + g(a_2 + g(a_3 + \cdots + g(a_n + x)\ldots)).$$

and the auxiliary expressions

$$T_0(x) = x, T_1(x) = g(a_n + x), T_2(x) = g(a_{n-1} + g(a_n + x)),$$
$$\ldots, T_{n-1}(x) = g(a_2 + g(a_3 + \cdots + g(a_n + x)\ldots)).$$

Then we get

$$|T_0(1) - T_0(0)| = 1$$
$$|T_{n-1}(1) - T_{n-1}(0)| = |S_n(1) - S_n(0)| = D_n.$$

Now

$$|T_k(1) - T_k(0)| = |\int_{a_{n-k+1}+T_{k-1}(0)}^{a_{n-k+1}+T_{k-1}(1)} g'(x)dx| \le$$

$$\le |\int_{a_{n-k+1}+T_{k-1}(0)}^{a_{n-k+1}+T_{k-1}(1)} dx| \le |T_{k-1}(1) - T_{k-1}(0)|, k = 1, 2, \ldots, n-1.$$

Therefore

$$D_n \le |T_k(1) - T_k(0)| \le |T_{k-1}(1) - T_{k-1}(0)| \le 1.$$

Note that $D_{n+1} \le D_n$. Hence there exists a number $k = k(n)$ such that the pair of numbers $|T_k(1) - T_k(0)|$ and $|T_{k-1}(1) - T_{k-1}(0)|$ satisfies

$$0 \le |T_{k-1}(1) - T_{k-1}(0)| - |T_k(1) - T_k(0)| \le \frac{1 - D_n}{n - 1}.$$

Kakeya then considers the sequences $(a_{n-k+1}+T_{k-1}(0))$ and $(a_{n-k+1}+T_{k-1}(1))$. Since these sequences are bounded he concludes that

$$l_0 = \lim(a_{n-k+1} + T_{k-1}(0))$$
$$l_1 = \lim(a_{n-k+1} + T_{k-1}(1))$$

both exist in a common subsequence. This leads to the equation

$$|l_1 - l_0| = |\int_{l_0}^{l_1} g'(x)dx|$$

Since $|g'(x)| < 1$ almost everywhere one sees that $l_1 - l_0 = 0$
From $0 \leq D_n \leq |(a_{n-k+1} + T_{k-1}(1)) - (a_{n-k+1} + T_{k-1}(0)|$ in a subsequence we obtain $\lim_{n\to\infty} D_n = 0$ generally!
From this result Kakeya deduces

(1) $\lim_{n\to\infty} S_n(0) =: S = a_1 + g(a_2 + g(a_3 + \cdots + g(a_n + \cdots)))$.

(2) $\lim_{n\to\infty} S_n(x) = S$. This convergence is uniformly for $0 \leq x \leq 1$.

(3) If ω has the notation (a_n) then $\lim_{n\to\infty} (a_1 + g(a_3 + \cdots + g(a_n + \cdots))) = \omega$.

(4) Different numbers cannot have the same notation.

Next he considers an arbitrary sequence (a_n) of the first kind and puts

$$U := g(a_2 + g(a_3 + \cdots + g(a_n + \cdots)))$$

Note that more common is the notation a_0 for the first digit, since this digit is just an integer and no restriction applies! He shows that for case A the equality $U = 1$ takes place when and only when $a_n = \beta - 1$ for all $n \geq 2$. A lengthier discussion gives a similar result for case B, namely: if (a_n) is of the first kind $U = 1$ when and only when if $a_n = \beta$ for $n \equiv 0 \mod 2$ and $a_n = \alpha - 1$ for $n \equiv 1 \mod 2$. This leads Kakeya to his definition of a *normal* sequence which is now better called an *admissible* sequence. He finally states his theorem.
Any number ω has its notation (a_n) which is normal. And conversely any normal sequence (a_n) corresponds uniquely to a number ω whose notation is (a_n).
In the final sections Kakeya shows that his results can be extended to the case $\alpha = -\infty$ or $\beta = \infty$. He further considers some examples.

(1) $f(x) = cx^r, c \in \mathbb{Z}$, such that either $r = 1$, $|c| \geq 2$ or $r < 1$, $|cr| \geq 1$.

   (1.1) $c = 10$, $r = 1$ leads to $f(x) = 10x$. This gives the decimal expansion

$$\omega = a_1 + \frac{a_2}{10} + \frac{a_3}{10^2} + \dots$$

     Note that $a_2, a_3, .. \in \{0, 1, ..., 9\}$.

   (1.2) $c = 1$, $r = -1$ leads to $f(x) = \frac{1}{x}$. Here we obtain continued fractions

$$\omega = a_1 + \cfrac{1}{a_2 + \cfrac{1}{a_3 + \dots}}.$$

     The algorithm implies that all a_j for $j \geq 2$ are positive integers.

   (1.3) $c = 2$, $r = \frac{1}{2}$ gives to $f(x) = 2\sqrt{x}$.

(2) $f(x) = c^x$, $c \in \mathbb{Z}$, $c \geq 3$

This example gives a representation of the form

$$\omega = a_1 + \log_c(a_2 + \log_c(a_3 + \dots + \log_c(a_n + \dots)))$$

.

Chapter 6

The cotangent algorithm

The starting point of Lehmer's paper [Lehmer 1938] is an unusual viewpoint. The *continued iteration* of a rational function $f(x, y)$ of two variables provides an algorithm for the expression of a real number as a sequence of rational numbers. Lehmer considers the iteration in the form

$$f(x_1, f(x_2, f(x_3, ...)))$$

and reminds the reader first to well known or less well known examples. The function $f(x, y) = x + y$ becomes an infinite series and for $f(x, y) = xy$ we get infinite products. For $f(x, y) = x + \frac{1}{y}$ we obtain regular continued fractions. The function $f(x, y) = x + \frac{y}{c}$ generates expansions to base c. He further mentions $f(x, y) = x(1 - y)$ which gives an algorithm discussed in [Pierce 1929] which paper we will explain first. Pierce's paper is very short. He considers series expansions of the form

$$x = q_1 - q_1 q_2 + q_1 q_2 q_3 - ...$$

where he supposes that the right members of this series are monotonically decreasing. He specializes to the case where starting with $x_0 = x$, $0 < x < 1$, one chooses p_n as the greatest positive integer such that $1 - p_n x_n > 0$ and

$$x_{n+1} = 1 - p_n x_n.$$

Therefore

$$1 + p_n \geq \frac{1}{x_n} > p_n$$

which implies $x_n \geq x_{n+1}$. Pierce remarks that rational numbers are periodic expansions but he seems to overlook that the algorithm demands $p_{n+1} \geq p_n$.

Therefore the only case of periodicity is that $x_n = \frac{1}{q}$ from a certain point on. This shows that this algorithm is similar to Engel's series. The at his time important application to algebraic numbers is illustrated with the root x of the equation $x^3 - 5x + 2 = 0$. He finds

$$x = \frac{1}{2} - \frac{1}{10} + \frac{1}{70} - \frac{1}{13790} + \ldots$$

Lehmer's paper is concerned with

$$f(x, y) = \frac{1 + xy}{y - x}$$

(or $\operatorname{arccot} f(x, y) = \operatorname{arccot} x$ - $\operatorname{arccot} y$). This relies on the equality

$$\cot(\alpha + \beta) = \frac{\cot \alpha \cot \beta + 1}{\cot \alpha - \cot \beta}.$$

The *continued cotangent* ξ is said *regular* if

(a) $\xi = \cot \sum_{j=0}^{\infty} (-1)^j \operatorname{arccot} n_j$ or $\xi = \cot \sum_{j=0}^{N} (-1)^j \operatorname{arccot} n_j$
(b) n_j is an integer for all $j \geq 0$
(c) If the sum is infinite then $n_{j+1} \geq n_j^2 + n_j + 1$, $j \geq 0$. If the sum is finite then $n_{j+1} \geq n_j^2 + n_j + 1$, $0 \leq j \leq N - 2$, but $n_{j+1} > n_j^2 + n_j + 1$, $j = N - 1$. Since $n_j \geq 0$ we take $0 < \operatorname{arccot} n_j \leq \frac{\pi}{2}$.

The condition (c) for finite sums is to avoid ambiguity since if

$$n_N = n_{N-1}^2 + n_{N-1} + 1$$

the equation

$$\operatorname{arccot} n_{N-1} - \operatorname{arccot} n_N = \operatorname{arccot}(n_{N-1} + 1)$$

is valid. This is an analogue to continued fractions where we find

$$\cfrac{1}{(q_k - 1) + \cfrac{1}{1}} = \frac{1}{q_k}.$$

Therefore one may postulate $q_k \geq 2$ for the last digit.
Lehmer then proves that every infinite regular continued cotangent converges. If x is a given real number he then defines

$$x_0 = x, \quad n_0 = \lfloor x_0 \rfloor$$

$$x_{k+1} = \frac{x_k n_k + 1}{x_k - n_k}, \; n_{k+1} = \lfloor x_{k+1} \rfloor, \; k \geq 0.$$

This algorithm gives a regular continued cotangent and its sum is the given number x.

The following analogue to regular continued fractions is also true. The number x is rational or irrational according as its continued expansion is finite or not. If $\xi = \cot \sum_{j=0}^{N}(-1)^j \operatorname{arccot} n_j$ then ξ is rational. Now suppose that $x = \frac{p}{q}$ then $x_k = \frac{p_k}{q_k}$ is also rational. From

$$x_{k+1} = \frac{p_{k+1}}{q_{k+1}} = \frac{p_k n_k + q_k}{p_k - n_k q_k} = \frac{p_k n_k + q_k}{r_k}$$

with $n_k = \lfloor \frac{p_k}{q_k} \rfloor$ we see $r_k < q_k$. Since we suppose that the fraction $\frac{p_{k+1}}{q_{k+1}}$ is in its lowest terms we have the inequality $q_{k+1} \leq r_k < q_k$. This can happen only finitely many often. Hence the algorithm stops.

As usual convergents are defined as the curtate expansion of m terms

$$\sigma_m(x) = \cot \sum_{j=0}^{m-1}(-1)^j \operatorname{arccot} n_j = \frac{A_m}{B_m}, \; m \geq 1.$$

Starting with $A_0 = 1, B_0 = 0$ the recursion relations

$$A_{k+1} = A_k n_k - (-1)^k B_k$$

$$B_{k+1} = B_k n_k + (-1)^k A_k$$

are valid. Then

$$A_m + i B_m = \prod_{j=0}^{m-1} (n_j + (-1)^m i)$$

$$A_m B_{m+1} - B_m A m + 1 = (-1)^m (A_m^2 + B_m^2) = (-1)^m \prod_{j=0}^{m-1} (n_j^2 + 1).$$

The number

$$\eta = \cot(\operatorname{arccot} 0 - \operatorname{arccot} 1 + \operatorname{arccot} 3 - \operatorname{arccot} 13 + \operatorname{arccot} 183 - ...)$$

has the least rapidly convergent continued cotangent.

Further an algorithm is given to express a regular continued cotangent as an "irregular" continued fraction. If $x = \cot \sum_{j=0}^{\infty}(-1)^j \operatorname{arccot} n_j$ then

$$x = n_0 + \cfrac{n_0^2 + 1}{n_1 - n_0 + \cfrac{n_1^2 + 1}{n_2 - n_1 + ...}}.$$

For the number η we have $n_{k+1} - n_k = n_k^2 + 1$ starting with $n_0 = 0$. If one defines

$$a_0 = 1, a_1 = 1, ..., a_{k+1} = (n_k + n_{k-1} + 1)a_{k-1}, ...$$

then we see

$$a_{k+1}a_k = n_{k+1} - n_k = n_k^2 + 1.$$

The conversion formula now produces

$$\eta = \cfrac{1}{a_0 + \cfrac{1}{a_1 + \cfrac{1}{a_2 + ...}}}.$$

If $\frac{C_m}{D_m}$ is the m-th convergent of the continued fraction, then Lehmer shows

$$\left| \eta - \frac{C_m}{D_m} \right| < \frac{1}{D_m^3}.$$

Therefore Lehmer could use a theorem of Siegel and concluded that η does not satisfy a cubic equation with rational coefficients. Since in 1955 Roth proved that for any algebraic number ζ and any $\varepsilon > 0$ the Diophantine inequality

$$\left| \zeta - \frac{p}{q} \right| < \frac{1}{q^{2+\varepsilon}}, \varepsilon > 0$$

has only finitely many solutions ([Roth 1955], [Davenport & Roth 1955]; see also [Cassels 1957]) we now know that η is a transcendental number.

A recent paper on Lehmer's algorithm is [Rivoal 2007].

Leighton's generalization runs as follows [Leighton 1940]. Let $y = y_0$ be a real number and $a_1, a_2, a_3, ...$ an arbitrary sequence of positive integers. Then he defines

$$b_0 = \lfloor y_0 \rfloor, y_n = \frac{a_n}{y_{n-1} - b_{n-1}}, b_n = \lfloor y_n \rfloor, n \geq 1.$$

Clearly we have the relation

$$y_{n-1} = b_{n-1} + \frac{a_n}{y_n}, n \geq 1.$$

Observe that $b_n \geq a_n$. The associated continued fraction

$$y_0 = b_0 + \cfrac{a_1}{b_1 + \cfrac{a_2}{b_2 + ...}}$$

is called a *proper continued fraction*. By using induction (or by using matrices) one proves

$$y_0 = \frac{y_n A_{n-1} + a_n A_{n-2}}{y_n B_{n-1} + a_n B_{n-2}}$$

$$A_n = b_n A_{n-1} + a_n A_{n-2}, \; B_n = b_n B_{n-1} + a_n B_{n-2}$$

$$A_{n-1} B_{n-2} - A_{n-2} B_{n-1} = (-1)^n a_1 a_2 ... a_{n-1}.$$

Furthermore he obtains

$$\lim_{n \to \infty} \frac{A_n}{B_n} = y.$$

Conversely, a continued fraction of the form

$$b_0 + \cfrac{a_1}{b_1 + \cfrac{a_2}{b_2 + ...}}$$

is the proper continued fraction of a real number y if $b_n \geq a_n$. Clearly, if $a_n = 1$ for all $n \geq 1$ then we are back to regular continued fractions. Leighton gives some other examples.

(1) $a_{3n+1} = 1, a_{3n+2} = 2, a_{3n+3} = 3$

$$\sqrt{3} = 1 + \cfrac{1}{1 + \cfrac{2}{5 + \cfrac{3}{6 + \cfrac{1}{2 + \cfrac{2}{12 + \cfrac{3}{3 + ...}}}}}}$$

(period length $= 6$, the periodicity starts with $y_3 = y_9$).

(2)

$$\frac{\sqrt{5} + 1}{2} = 1 + \cfrac{2}{3 + \cfrac{2}{8 + \cfrac{2}{4 + ...}}}$$

(period length $= 2$, $y_2 = y_4$)

(3)

$$\frac{\sqrt{17} + 3}{2} = 3 + \cfrac{2}{3 + \cfrac{2}{3 + ...}}$$

(period length $= 1$).

The first impression of the paper is that $a_1, a_2, a_3, \ldots$ is a given sequence but Leighton gives an example for coupling.

$$r_0 = b_0, \ r_n = r_{n-1} + b_n, \ a_n = r_{n+1}^2 + 1.$$

He claims that this is Lehmer's cotangent algorithm [Lehmer 1938] but this is not exactly true. If $k < x \leq k + 1$ then Leighton's choice defines the map

$$Tx = \frac{k^2 + 1}{x - k}$$

but Lehmer's algorithm reads

$$Tx = \frac{xk + 1}{x - k} = k + \frac{k^2 + 1}{x - k}.$$

Chapter 7

Bissinger and Everett

In 1943 Bissinger presented his paper [Bissinger 1944] to the American Mathematical Society. He quotes [Pierce 1929], [Lehmer 1938], and [Leighton 1940] as generalizations and analogues of regular continued fractions but not [Kakeya 1924]. He obviously did not know this paper. He starts with a function $f : [1, \infty [\rightarrow] 0, 1]$ with the properties

(1) $f(1) = 1$

(2) f is strictly decreasing

(3) $\lim_{t \to \infty} f(t) = 0$

(4) If $1 \leq t_1 < t_2$ then $|f(t_2) - f(t_1)| < |t_2 - t_1|$

(5) There is a constant $\lambda, 0 < \lambda < 1$ with the property: If $1 + f(2) < t_1 < t_2$ then $|f(t_2) - f(t_1)| < \lambda^2 |t_2 - t_1|$.

Now let $0 < x < 1$. Three sequences $(z_n), (\theta_n)$ and (a_n) are defined by the definitions

$$x = f(z_0)$$
$$a_n = [z_{n-1}], n \geq 1$$
$$\theta_n = z_{n-1} - a_n, n \geq 1$$
$$\theta_n = f(z_n).$$

Note that (4) implies the continuity of f. Therefore the sequence (z_n) is well defined. If $\theta_1, \ldots, \theta_{k-1} \neq 0$ while $\theta_k = 0$ then $a_k \geq 2$ and

$$x = f(a_1 + f(a_2 + \ldots + f(a_k)))$$

the expression on the right called the f-*expansion* x. If $\theta_n \neq 0$ for all $n \geq 1$ then he calls the expression

$$f(a_1 + f(a_2 + \ldots))$$

the f-*expansion* of x. He now introduces

$$\varphi_n(t) = f(a_1 + f(a_2 + \ldots + f(a_n + t)))$$

and $x_n = \varphi_n(0)$.

The following lemma is immediate

If $n \equiv 1 \pmod 2$ then $\varphi_n(t)$ is decreasing in t.

If $n \equiv 0 \pmod 2$ then $\varphi_n(t)$ is increasing in t.

From this he deduces without effort

$$0 < x_2 < x_4 < \ldots \leq x \leq \ldots < x_3 < x_1 \leq 1.$$

It is evident if $\lim\limits_{n \to \infty} x_n$ exists then $\lim\limits_{n \to \infty} x_n = x$.

All this is very similar to Kakeya's considerations if one replaces Bissinger's function f by Kakeya's g. Bissinger presents a different proof of convergence which is modeled after the proof for regular fractions, i.e. $f(x) = \frac{1}{x}$. Let $x_n = \varphi_n(0)$ and $y_n = \varphi_n(1)$ and $I(a_1, \ldots, a_n)$ the closed interval with endpoints x_n and y_n. Then $x_{n+1} \in I(a_1, \ldots, a_n)$. The crucial element is the next lemma.

Let $A_n = \limsup\limits_{a_1, \ldots, a_n} |I(a_1, \ldots, a_n)|$ then $A_n < \lambda^{n-2}$. Here $|I|$ denotes the length of an interval I.

The proof runs as follows

$$A_{n+2} = \limsup_{n} |I(a_1, \ldots, a_n, a_{n+1}, a_{n+2})|$$

$$= \limsup_{n} \frac{|I(a_1, \ldots, a_n, a_{n+1}, a_{n+2})|}{|I(a_3, \ldots, a_{n+2})|} |I(a_3, \ldots, a_{n+2})|$$

$$\leq \limsup_{\substack{a_1, a_2 \geq 1 \\ 0 < u < v \leq 1}} \frac{|f(a_1 + f(a_2 + u)) - f(a_1 + f(a_2 + v))|}{|u - v|} . A_n$$

Now

$$\frac{|f(a_1 + f(a_2 + u)) - f(a_1 + f(a_2 + v))|}{|u - v|}$$

$$= \frac{|f(a_1 + f(a_2 + u)) - f(a_1 + f(a_2 + v))|}{|(a_1 + f(a_2 + u)) - (a_1 + f(a_2 + v))|} \cdot \frac{|f(a_2 + u) - f(a_2 + v)|}{|u - v|}$$

If $a_2 = 1$ then $a_1 + f(a_2 + u) > a_1 + f(a_2 + v) \geq 1 + f(2)$ and if $a_2 \geq 2 > 1 + f(2)$ condition (5) shows

$$A_{n+2} \leq \lambda^2 A_n.$$

This gives the following result.

$$|x_n - x| \leq \lambda^{n-2}.$$

Therefore the f-expansion of x converges to x.
Bissinger remarks that for regular continued fractions this result gives

$$\left| \frac{p_n(x)}{q_n(x)} - x \right| \leq \left(\frac{2}{3} \right)^{n-2}$$

which is similar in form to the best possible estimate

$$\left| \frac{p_n(x)}{q_n(x)} - x \right| \leq \left(\frac{3 - \sqrt{5}}{2} \right)^{n-1}$$

Bissinger further shows uniqueness for f-expansions.
To the end of his paper he considers piecewise linear functions. Let $1 = y_1 > y_2 > y_3 \ldots$ be a decreasing sequence of positive numbers with $\lim_{n \to \infty} y_n = 0$. Let f_p the function which joins the points (n, y_n) with linear pieces, i.e.

$$f_p(x) = y_n + (y_{n+1} - y_n)(x - n), n \leq x \leq n + 1.$$

He proves some theorems similar to the theorems of Borel and Bernstein [Borel 1909, Bernstein 1912] (see the chapter Around the theorem of Borel and Bernstein).

Everett's paper [Everett 1946] is intended as a follow-up to [Bissinger 1944]. In contrast he uses continuous strictly increasing functions $f : [0, p] \to [0, 1]$, $p \geq 2$ a fixed integer, $f(0) = 0$, and $f(p) = 1$. Let $\gamma_0 \geq 0$ a real number then a sequence (c_n) of integers is defined by

$$\gamma_0 = c_0 + f(\gamma_1), c_0 \leq \gamma_0 < c_0 + 1, 0 \leq \gamma_1 < p$$
$$\gamma_1 = c_1 + f(\gamma_2), c_1 \leq \gamma_1 < c_1 + 1, 0 \leq \gamma_2 < p$$

and so on. To avoid sequences terminating in $p - 1, p - 1, \ldots$ Everett then requires

$$f(p) - f(t) < p - t \text{ for } p - 1 \leq t < p.$$

This condition means that the function $f(t + p - 1)$ has no fixed point t with $0 < t < 1$.

Everett next discusses the case when the map $\gamma_0 \mapsto (c_0, c_1, c_2, \ldots)$ is not bijective (many-one case in his terminology), a discussion which is hardly reflected in the further literature (see [Parry 1964b]). Then he states several conditions for the map $\gamma_0 \mapsto (c_0, c_1, c_2, \ldots)$ being bijective (one-one correspondence). For the many-one case he gives the following example. Let $p = 3$ and let f be defined by $f(0) = 0, f\left(\frac{4}{3}\right) = \frac{1}{3}, f\left(\frac{5}{3}\right) = \frac{2}{3}, f(3) = 1$, and elsewhere by the broken line connecting these points. This is best written as the fibred system

$$Tx = 4x, \quad 0 \le x < \frac{1}{4}$$

$$Tx = 4x - 1, \quad \frac{1}{4} \le x \le \frac{1}{3}$$

$$Tx = x, \quad \frac{1}{3} \le x \le \frac{2}{3}$$

$$Tx = 4x - 2, \quad \frac{2}{3} \le x \le \frac{3}{4}$$

$$Tx = 4x - 3, \quad \frac{3}{4} \le x \le 1.$$

Therefore, one sees that on the middle interval $M =]\frac{1}{3}, \frac{2}{3}[$ all points have the same expansion. If one removes $\bigcup_{n=0}^{\infty} T^{-n} M$ a set similar to the famous Cantor middle-third set remains.

For the one-one case he gives the following examples.

1. $f(t) = \frac{t^n}{p^n}, p \ge 2$ an integer, $1 \le n < p$ a second integer. For $n = 1$ this gives the decimals with base p. If $q \le p - 2$ is an integer let αp be the limit of the f-expansion $(q, q, q, \ldots)$. Then

$$\alpha p = q + f(\alpha p)$$

or

$$\alpha p = q + \alpha^n.$$

Thus the equation $x^n - px + q = 0$, $1 \le n < p, 0 \le q \le p - 2$ has exactly one real root in $[0, 1[$, namely

$$\alpha = \frac{1}{p}(q + f(q + f(q + \ldots))).$$

In particular, for $n = 2, p = 3, q = 1$ the number $\alpha = \frac{3 - \sqrt{5}}{2}$ is approximately $\frac{1}{3}(1 + \frac{1}{9}(1 + \frac{1}{9}(1 + \frac{1}{9})^2)^2)$.

2. $f(t) = \sqrt[n]{1+t} - 1, p = 2^n - 1, n \geq 2$.
   We consider

   $$\gamma = 1 + f(q + f(q + \ldots))$$

   where $0 < q \leq 2^n - 2$. Then $\gamma = 1 + f(q + \gamma - 1)$ or $\gamma^n - \gamma - q = 0$. Thus the equation $x^n - x - q = 0, n \geq 2, 0 < q \leq 2^n - 2$, has exactly one root γ in $]1, 2]$. This is applied to $x^2 - x - 1 = 0$, $x^2 - x - 2 = 0$, and $x^3 - x - 6 = 0$.

   The associated algorithm is called Bolyai's algorithm in [Rényi 1957] (we will discuss this paper later).

The sequence of digits $a_1(x), a_2(x), a_3(x), \ldots$ can be seen as a sequence of *random variables*. Then the question about their distribution arises. This problem is intimately connected with the *ergodic properties* of the map $Tx = f^{-1}x - \lfloor f^{-1}x \rfloor$ which will be considered in other chapters. Here we mention the converse problem. Let ν be a *non-atomic probability measure* on $[0, 1]$ such that its cumulative distribution function $F(x) = \nu([0, x[)$ is strictly increasing. Furthermore let p_n be a given sequence of probabilities. Can one construct a function f so that the distribution of the the digits a_n under the measure ν is just p_n? We refer to the papers [Guthery 1970], [Spătaru 1977, 1978], and [Kinney & Pitcher 1965]. A separate chapter will be devoted to the important paper [Rényi 1957] and some of his followers.

We mention the paper [Rechard 1950]. If the increasing function f defines an f-expansion for the number γ with digits $c_1, c_2, c_3, \ldots, 0 \leq c_j \leq p-1, j \geq 1$ then he defines an *associated function*

$$F(\gamma) = \sum_{j=1}^{\infty} \frac{c_j}{p^j}.$$

He shows that this function F is characterized by the functional equation

$$F(f(x)) = \frac{\lfloor x \rfloor}{p} + \frac{F(x - \lfloor x \rfloor)}{p}.$$

On the other hand if F is a continuous strictly increasing function then there is a unique function f^* which defines a suitable f-expansion, namely

$$f^*(x) = F^{-1}\left(\frac{\lfloor x \rfloor + F(x - \lfloor x \rfloor)}{p}\right).$$

An example is the following. Let $p = 2$ and $F(x) = x^n$ then

$$f^*(x) = \frac{x}{\sqrt[n]{2}}, \quad 0 \leq x \leq 1$$

$$f^*(x) = \frac{\lfloor (x-1)^n + 1 \rfloor^{\frac{1}{n}}}{\sqrt[n]{2}}, \ 1 \leq x \leq 2.$$

In this way the dyadic expansion $R = 0.r_1 r_2 r_3...$ is associated to

$$\sqrt[n]{R} = f^*(r_1 + f^*(r_2 + f^*(r_3 + ...))).$$

Chapter 8

Around the theorem of Borel and Bernstein

At the beginning of his important paper [Borel 1909] Borel explains in chapter one that two categories of problems are distinguished: «probabilités discontinues»(with finitely many outcomes) and «probabilités continues ou géometriques»(with infinitely many outcomes). This distinction is felt to be incomplete. Due to (at Borel's time recent) results of set theory one has to distinguish between the continuum and countable sets. Borel now concentrates on probabilities with countably many outcomes. It is interesting that he says that countable sets are the only sets we can really attack and the continuum is a transitory instrument for studying that reality. Then he starts to study the case where the number of possible outcomes is at most countable and the number of samples also is at most countable. However, without stating it explicitly he assumes stochastic independence since he uses the *product rule*. This rule says that the probability of the occurrence of the events A and B at the same time is the product of their probabilities, i. e. $P(A \cap B) = P(A)P(B)$.
If for an integer $q \geq 2$

$$x = \sum_{n=1}^{\infty} \frac{b_n}{q^n}, \, 0 \leq b_j < q, \, j = 1, 2, 3, \ldots$$

Borel assumes that the digits are independent and every digit has the probability $\frac{1}{q}$. He says that these assumptions are equivalent to the probability of being $x \in [a, b]$ is equal to $b - a$. He mentions the *favorable case* $b_n(x) = 3$ (for the base $q = 10$). Then the probability that $b_n(x) = 3$ for infinitely many

43

values of n is 1. The probability that $b_n(x) = 3$ for all $n \geq 1$ is zero but since

$$\frac{1}{3} = \sum_{n=1}^{\infty} \frac{3}{10^n}, \ 0 \leq b_j < q, \ j = 1, 2, 3, \ldots$$

probability zero is not equivalent to impossibility.

Next he considers $p = 2$ and shows that the probability of the ratio of the appearance of 0 and 1 equals 1, i. e.

$$\lim_{N \to \infty} \frac{\#\{1 \leq n \leq N : b_n(x) = 1\}}{\#\{1 \leq n \leq N : b_n(x) = 0\}} = 1.$$

Then he considers the frequencies of digits in the base $q = 10$. Let

$$c_k = \#\{1 \leq n \leq N : b_n(x) = k\}$$

then a number x is called *simply normal* if

$$\lim_{N \to \infty} \frac{c_k}{N} = \frac{1}{10}.$$

A number x is called (totally) *normal* if it is simply normal with respect to every base $10, 10^2, 10^3, \ldots$. This can also be expressed in the following form. Let A_N be the number of the appearance of a fixed block of digits of length p then

$$\lim_{N \to \infty} \frac{A_N}{N} = \frac{1}{10^p}.$$

[Champernowne 1933] gave the first explicit example of a normal number, namely

$$\xi = 0.1234567891011121314....$$

This number is formed by just writing down all natural numbers in increasing order.

If a number is normal with respect to all bases $q \geq 2$ it is called *absolutely normal*. Borel sketches a proof that the probability for a number being absolutely normal equals to 1. He gives a method for constructing numbers which are normal to base 10. However, this construction is not easy to follow. More on normal numbers can be found in [Bugeaud 2012].

A new chapter in the question of normal numbers was opened by the so-called BBP-formula for π [Bailey & Borwein & Plouffe 1997], namely

$$\pi = \sum_{j=0}^{\infty} \frac{1}{16^j} \left(\frac{4}{8j+1} - \frac{2}{8j+4} - \frac{1}{8j+5} - \frac{1}{8j+6} \right).$$

This formula permits to calculate binary or hexadecimal digits of π beginning at an arbitrary position. The proof is elementary! For $k < 8$ we find

$$\int_0^{\frac{1}{\sqrt{2}}} \frac{x^{k-1}}{1-x^8} dx = \int_0^{\frac{1}{\sqrt{2}}} \sum_{j=0}^{\infty} x^{k-1-8j} dx = \frac{1}{2^{\frac{k}{2}}} \sum_{j=0}^{\infty} \frac{1}{16^j(8j+k)}.$$

Then

$$\sum_{j=0}^{\infty} \frac{1}{16^j} \left(\frac{4}{8j+1} - \frac{2}{8j+4} - \frac{1}{8j+5} - \frac{1}{8j+6} \right)$$

$$= \int_0^{\frac{1}{\sqrt{2}}} \frac{4\sqrt{2} - 8x^3 - 4\sqrt{2}x^4 - 8x^5}{1-x^8} dx = \int_0^1 \frac{16y-16}{y^4 - 2y^3 + 4y - 4} dy$$

$$= \int_0^1 \frac{16y-16}{y^4 - 2y^3 + 4y - 4} dy = \int_0^1 \frac{4y}{y^2-2} dy - \int_0^1 \frac{4y-8}{y^2-2y+2} dy = \pi.$$

We used the substitution $y = \sqrt{2}x$.

The detection of BBP-formulas for various constants has given a new incentive to the question of normality (see [Bailey & Borwein & Mattingly & Wightwick 2013]).

Coming back to Borel's paper we mention that he made some remarks on periodic decimal fractions and on quadratic equations.

From the viewpoint of f-expansions the most interesting part is chapter three on continued fractions. Borel starts with calculating p_{ik}, the probability that $a_i(x) = k$. If $a_1 = k$ then $\frac{1}{k+1} < x < \frac{1}{k}$ and

$$p_{1k} = \frac{1}{k(k+1)}.$$

If $a_2 = k$ then

$$p_{2k} = \sum_{n=1}^{\infty} \frac{1}{(nk+n+1)(nk+1)} = \frac{\pi^2}{6k(k+1)}(1 - \epsilon_k)$$

where $\lim_{k\to\infty} \epsilon_k = 0$. He even calculates p_{3k} but says that further calculations are complicated but not helpful. By the way: It is not stated that the a_n are not stochastically independent. If

$$\frac{P_n}{Q_n} = \cfrac{1}{a_1 + \cfrac{1}{a_2 + ... + \cfrac{1}{a_n}}}$$

then he observes

$$p_{nk} = \left| \frac{P_{n-2} + kP_{n-1}}{Q_{n-2} + kQ_{n-1}} - \frac{P_{n-2} + (k+1)P_{n-1}}{Q_{n-2} + (k+1)Q_{n-1}} \right|.$$

This allows to deduce

$$\frac{2}{3k(k+1)} < p_{nk} < \frac{3}{(k+1)(k+2)}.$$

Let $P_{nk} = p_{n1} + \ldots + p_{nk}$, the probability that $a_n \le k$. Since

$$1 - P_{nk} = p_{n,k+1} + p_{n,k+2}\ldots$$

he obtains

$$1 - \frac{3}{k+3} < P_{nk} < 1 - \frac{2}{3(k+1)}.$$

Let $\phi(n) > 0$ be an increasing function such that $\sum_{n=1}^{\infty} \frac{1}{\phi(n)}$ is convergent. Then the series $\sum_{n=1}^{\infty}(1 - P_{n,\phi(n)})$ is also convergent. This proves the first part of the so-called *Theorem of Borel-Bernstein*. If $\sum_{n=1}^{\infty} \frac{1}{\phi(n)}$ is convergent then the probability that $a_n > \phi(n)$ infinitely often is 0. In other words: The probability that $a_n < \phi(n)$ for $n \ge n(x)$ equals 1. From this result he deduces that

$$\lim_{n\to\infty} \frac{a_n}{\phi(n)} = 0$$

has probability 1 (one can also say: it is true *almost everywhere*). The sketchy argument seems to assume that the digits a_n are stochastically independent. However the result is true.

If $\sum_{n=1}^{\infty} \frac{1}{\phi(n)}$ is divergent he claims that the relation

$$\limsup_{n\to\infty} \frac{a_n}{\phi(n)} = \infty$$

is true with probability 1.

In the theory of planetary motions there is the problem under which conditions an equation

$$\sum_{\nu=1}^{n} r_\nu e^{i(g_\nu t + h_\nu)} = r e^{i(ct + \chi(t))}, \; r_\nu > 0, g_\nu, h_\nu \text{ constants}$$

holds where c is constant and the function $\chi(t)$ is bounded. The expression on the right side is called the *mean motion*. Lagrange has shown that sufficient conditions are (1) $n = 2$ or (2): There is a value $r = r_1$, say, such that $r_1 > r_2 + ... + r_\nu$. Piers Bohl has dealt with the case $n = 3$ [Bohl 1909]. Bernstein first proposes in [Bernstein 1912] the axiom that for values which can be obtained by physical experiments one should neglect null sets. In this way he reduces the problem of Lagrange and Bohl to a question of metrical number theory. He eventually concludes that there is no mean motion.

We look at the central part, namely Bernstein's metrical theory of continued fractions. For a continued fraction

$$x = \cfrac{1}{a_1 + \cfrac{1}{a_2 + ...}}$$

the numbers x for which $a_1, a_2, ..., a_{n-1}$ are fixed but $a_n \geq k$ lie in an interval of length

$$l_{nk} = \frac{1}{Q_{n-1}(kQ_{n-1} + Q_{n-2})}.$$

This gives

$$\frac{1}{k} < \frac{l_{nk}}{l_{n1}} < \frac{2}{k+1}.$$

He defines A_{nk} and B_{nk} as the *geometric probabilities* (this the Lebesgue measure of the corresponding sets) that $a_n < k$ and $a_n \geq k$. Then

$$\frac{k-1}{k+1} < A_{nk} < \frac{k-1}{k}$$

and

$$\frac{1}{k} < B_{nk} < \frac{2}{k+1}.$$

The probability $A_{n_1 k, ..., n_r k}$ that for $n_1 < n_2 < ... < n_r$ the inequalities

$$a_{n_1} < k, a_{n_2} < k, ..., a_{n_r} < k$$

hold satisfies (for $k \geq 2$)

$$\left(\frac{k-1}{k+1}\right)^r < A_{n_1 k, ..., n_r k} < \left(\frac{k-1}{k}\right)^r.$$

Then he finds that the probability $B_{n_1 k, ..., n_r k}$ for the conditions

$$k \leq a_{n_1}, k \leq a_{n_2}, ..., k \leq a_{n_r} < k$$

satisfies (for $k \geq 2$) the inequality

$$\left(\frac{1}{k}\right)^r < B_{n_1 k, \ldots, n_r k} < \left(\frac{2}{k+1}\right)^r \leq \left(\frac{k}{k+1}\right)^r.$$

This inequality gives the following result. The numbers $x \in [0, 1]$ which satisfy $a_{n_j} < k$ or $a_{n_j} \geq k$ in a fixed subsequence $n_1 < n_2 < n_3 < \ldots$ form sets N_k and $\overline{N_k}$ of measure zero.

The set $N = \bigcup_k N_k$ is also a nullset.

He furthermore proves (using a very unlucky notation which we avoid) that there is a set M of measure 1 such that for any $x \in M$ there exists a sequence $\nu_1 < \nu_2 < \nu_3 < \ldots$ and an associated sequence

$$b_1 < b_2 < b_3 < \ldots$$

such that

$$\frac{\nu_i x - \lfloor \nu_i x \rfloor}{\nu_i} < \frac{1}{\nu_i^2 b_i}, \text{ for all } i \geq 1.$$

The numbers ν_i are a subsequence of the denominators Q_n and the numbers b_i a subsequence of the digits of the continued fraction expansion. He also remarks that the set of numbers which contain $a_n = 1$ infinitely many often has measure 1.

If one considers the subsequence which obeys the condition $a_n < \varphi(n)$ then it is easy to see that

$$\prod_{\nu=1}^{n+r} \left(1 - \frac{2}{\varphi(\nu) + 1}\right) < A_{n\varphi(n), n+1\varphi(n+1), \ldots, n+r\varphi(n+r)} < \prod_{\nu=1}^{n+r} \left(1 - \frac{1}{\varphi(\nu)}\right).$$

If $\sum_{n=1}^{\infty} \frac{1}{\varphi(n)}$ is convergent then the product $w = \prod_{\nu=1}^{\infty} (1 - \frac{1}{\varphi(\nu)})$ is convergent and its value $w \neq 0$. If $\sum_{n=1}^{\infty} \frac{1}{\varphi(n)}$ is divergent then

$$\overline{A} = \lim_{r \to \infty} A_{n\varphi(n), n+1\varphi(n+1), \ldots, n+r\varphi(n+r)} = 0.$$

Similar considerations are valid for the condition $a_n \geq \varphi(n)$. So he states the *Theorem of Borel-Bernstein* (as it was later called) in the following form. The necessary and sufficient condition for the fact that $\varphi(n)$ is an upper (or lower) bound for $n \geq n_0$ with a probability $0 < w < 1$ is the convergence of $\sum_{n=1}^{\infty} \frac{1}{\varphi(n)}$.

Let us give a few comments on this part of the theorem. If

$$M_N = \{x : a_n < \varphi(n) \text{ for all } n \geq N\}$$

then $\lambda(M_N) > 0$. This is correct. However, the remark on the lower bound is not correct and the inequalities given for some related sets $B_{n_1 k, \ldots, n_r k}$ do not give a convergent product for the estimate from below.

If $\sum_{n=1}^{\infty} \frac{1}{\varphi(n)}$ is divergent then with probability 1 the bounding inequality is broken for infinitely many values of n.

The other part considers the set

$$F = \{x : a_n \geq \varphi(n) \text{ for infinitely many values of } n\}$$

and the assertion $\lambda(F) = 1$ is correct.

A good exposition of these results can be found in the nice book [Khintchine 1963]. We will see that the map $Tx = \frac{1}{x} - \lfloor \frac{1}{x} \rfloor$ is *ergodic*. Then clearly the set F is invariant and therefore has measure 0 or 1. The set M_N is not invariant and can therefore have a measure w, $0 < w < 1$.

Chapter 9

Measure zero or one

Let us recall that a set $E \subseteq [0,1]$ has measure $\lambda(E) = 0$ if for any $\varepsilon > 0$ there are countably many intervals $E_1, E_2, E_3, \ldots$ such that

$$E \subseteq \bigcup_{j=1}^{\infty} E_j, \ \sum_{j=1}^{\infty} \lambda(E_j) < \varepsilon.$$

For illustration we show that the set

$$E_7 = \{x = \sum_{j=1}^{\infty} \frac{\varepsilon_j}{10^j} : \varepsilon_j \neq 7 \text{ for all} j \geq 1\}$$

is a null set, i. e. $\lambda(E_7) = 0$. There are 9^n cylinders $B(\varepsilon_1, \varepsilon_2, \ldots, \varepsilon_n)$ with the property $\varepsilon_j \neq 7$, $1 \leq j \leq n$. These cylinders are intervals of length 10^{-n}. Clearly E_7 is contained in their union. Therefore

$$\lambda(E_7) \leq \frac{9^n}{10^n} = \left(\frac{9}{10}\right)^n < \epsilon$$

if $n \geq n_0$.

In the year 1915 Jacobsthal and Knopp introduced the notion of *homogeneous sets* („homogene Mengen") [Jacobsthal & Knopp 1915]. Knopp later proved the following theorem which we will simplify for our purpose [Knopp 1926]. Let $I = [\alpha, \beta]$ be an arbitrary interval then the expression

$$D(I) = \frac{\lambda(E \cap I)}{\beta - \alpha}$$

is called the *mean outer density* of E relative to I. Knopp works with the more general concept of an *outer measure* but we restrict our attention to *measurable sets* (we will come back to this notion in the chapter on invariant measures). A set E is called *homogeneous* if the density of E relative to any interval has the constant value d. Then it is not difficult to see that for every homogeneous set only $d = 0$ or $d = 1$ occur. Therefore if there is a number θ such that $D(I) \leq \theta < 1$ then $d = 0$. If there is a number γ such that $0 < \gamma \leq D(I)$ then $d = 1$.

Knopp's theorem reads as follows. Let $E \subseteq [0,1]$ and assume that every interval $[\alpha, \beta] \subseteq [0,1]$ can be partitioned in countably many intervals $i_1, i_2, i_3, \ldots$ such that $i_k \cap i_{k+1}$ contains at most one point, $\sum_{k=1}^{\infty} \lambda(i_k) = \beta - \alpha$, and $i_\nu \cap E$ is geometrically similar to E then E is homogeneous.

The last condition is reminiscent of the later notion of *self-similarity*. Geometrically similar means that $E \cap i_\nu = \kappa_\nu (E \cap [\alpha, \beta]) + \delta_\nu$ for some constants $0 < \kappa_\nu \leq 1$ and δ_ν. Then

$$D(i_\nu) = \frac{\lambda(E \cap i_\nu)}{\lambda(i_\nu)} = \frac{\kappa_\nu \lambda(E \cap I)}{\kappa_\nu \lambda(I)} = D(I).$$

Knopp just remarks that geometrically similar sets have the same density. Therefore $\lambda(E \cap i_\nu) = D(I)\lambda(i_\nu)$.

Knopp first considers „Systembrüche", i. e. numbers

$$x = \sum_{j=1}^{\infty} \frac{\varepsilon_j}{2^j}, \, \varepsilon_j \in \{0,1\}.$$

He remarks that base 2 clearly can be replaced by any positive integer $g \geq 2$. He then introduces

$$x_0 = x, \, x_p = \sum_{j=1}^{\infty} \frac{\varepsilon_{j+p}}{2^j} = 2^p x - \lfloor 2^p x \rfloor, \, p \geq 1.$$

The main result is the following.

Let E be a measurable set with the property that either $x_p \in E$ for all $p \geq 0$ or $x_p \in [0,1] \setminus E$ for all $p \geq 0$ then E is homogeneous. The proof is easy! Every interval I can be written as a union of intervals of the form $[\frac{k}{2^p}, \frac{k+1}{2^p}]$, $p \geq 0$, $0 \leq k < 2^p - 1$ (since the rational numbers form a set of measure 0 we can discard them). Note that

$$x = \frac{k + x_p}{2^p}.$$

Therefore $I \cap E$ and $[\frac{k}{2^p}, \frac{k+1}{2^p}] \cap E$ are geometrically similar.

Note that Knopp's condition is implied by *ergodicity*. A map $T : [0,1] \to [0,1]$ is called *ergodic* if $T^{-1}E = E$ implies $\lambda(E) = 0$ or $\lambda(E) = 1$. This condition was also called *metrically transitive* and *indecomposable* (see [Martin 1934] and [Ryll-Nardzewski 1951]). Knopp then applies his results to the number

$$E(n, x) = \#\{1 \le j \le n : \varepsilon_j(x) = 1\}.$$

He shows that the set $E = \{x \in [0, 1] : E(n, x) = \frac{n}{2} + O(\sqrt{n})\}$ has measure 0. This result was already shown in [Hardy & Littlewood 1914]. Khintchine has shown that the set

$$F = \{x \in [0, 1] : E(n, x) = \frac{n}{2} + O(\sqrt{n \log \log n})\}$$

satisfies $\lambda(F) = 1$ [Khintchine 1923].
Then Knopp considers continued fractions. If

$$x = x_0 = \cfrac{1}{b_1 + \cfrac{1}{b_2 + \dots}}$$

and

$$x_p = \cfrac{1}{b_{p+1} + \cfrac{1}{b_{p+2} + \dots}}$$

then he proves the corresponding result.
Let E be a measurable set with the property that either $x_p \in E$ for all $p \ge 0$ or $x_p \in [0, 1] \setminus E$ for all $p \ge 0$ then E is homogeneous. He introduces the map

$$m(x) = \frac{ax + b}{cx + d}$$

where a, b, c, d are non-negative integers such that $|ad - bc| = 1$ and either $a = 0$, $b = c = d = 1$ or $0 < c < d$. If the set E has density $\delta < 1$ in the interval $[0, 1]$ then the set $m(E)$ has density $\delta' \le \frac{1+\delta}{2} < 1$ in the interval with endpoints $\frac{b}{d}$ and $\frac{a+b}{b+d}$. This implies that the map $Tx = \frac{1}{x} - \lfloor \frac{1}{x} \rfloor$ is *ergodic*. Knopp then refers to already known results which have in common that they are correct for a set of numbers with measure 0 or 1. Then he gives a probably new result. Every natural number appears infinitely many often in the continued fraction of almost all numbers.
If $\theta_{n,k} = \lambda(\{x \in [0, 1] : b_n = k\})$ then he shows

$$\frac{2}{3k(k+1)} \le \theta_{n,k} \le \frac{3}{(k+1)(k+2)}.$$

If $\eta_{n,k} = \lambda(\{x \in [0,1] : b_n \neq k\})$ then

$$1 - \frac{3}{(k+1)(k+2)} \leq \eta_{n.k} \leq 1 - \frac{2}{3k(k+1)}.$$

If $M_m(k) = \{x \in [0,1] : b_m \neq k\}$ then

$$\mathcal{M}_n(k) = \bigcap_{m \geq n} M_m(k) = \{x \in [0,1] : b_m \neq k \text{ for } m \geq n\}.$$

Hence we obtain $\lambda(\mathcal{M}_n(k)) \leq 1 - \frac{2}{3k(k+1)}$. Since $\mathcal{M}_n(k) \subseteq \mathcal{M}_{n+1}(k)$ we find
that for $\mathcal{M}(k) = \lim_n \mathcal{M}_n(k)$ we also have $\lambda(\mathcal{M}(k)) \leq 1 - \frac{2}{3k(k+1)}$.
But $\mathcal{M}(k) = \{x : b_n(x) \neq k \text{ for } n \geq n(x)\}$ is a homogeneous set. Therefore $\lambda(\mathcal{M}(k)) = 0$. Therefore since $\bigcup_{k=1}^{\infty} \mathcal{M}(k)$ is also a nullset the set
$\{x : b_n(x) \neq k \text{ infinitely often}\}$ has measure 1.

An interesting variant of the proof that the map

$$Tx = \frac{1}{x} - \lfloor \frac{1}{x} \rfloor$$

is ergodic is given in [Martin 1934]. A set of transformations which leave a p-
dimensional region $G \subseteq \mathbb{R}^n$ (the letter G remembers the German word *Gebiet*,
an open connected set) is called *metrically transitive* if the complement of an
invariant subset with positive measure is a nullset. The principal result of the
paper is to show that the *elliptic modular group*

$$\zeta = \frac{\alpha z + \beta}{\gamma z + \delta}$$

where the numbers $\alpha, \beta, \gamma, \delta$ are integers for which $\alpha\delta - \beta\gamma = 1$ and ζ, z are
complex variables is metrically transitive on the real axis (here Martin takes
$n = 2$ and $p = 1$). We observe that the group of all real maps

$$\xi = \frac{\alpha x + \beta}{\gamma x + \delta}$$

contains the translations $\xi = x + k$, $k \in \mathbb{Z}$. If $S \subseteq \mathbb{R}$ is an invariant set with
$\lambda(S) > 0$ it is enough to show that $S_1 = S \cap]0,1]$ has Lebesgue measure $\lambda(S_1) =$
1. Let $\xi \in]0,1]$ be an irrational number and denote by $\xi = [p_1, p_2, p_3, ...]$ its
development into an unending regular continued fraction. Martin then uses
convergents $\frac{P_n}{Q_n} = [p_1, p_2, ..., p_n]$ and the interval $I^{(n)} =]\frac{P_{2n}}{Q_{2n}}, \frac{P_{2n-1}+P_{2n}}{Q_{2n-1}+Q_{2n}}[$ (a

cylinder of rank n in the language of fibred systems). He gives the weak estimate $\lambda(I^{(n)}) < \frac{1}{2n}$. The transformation

$$T_n x = \frac{P_{2n-1}x + P_{2n}}{Q_{2n-1}x + Q_{2n}}$$

belongs to the elliptic modular group. He defines

$$\phi_n(x) = \frac{1}{(Q_{2n-1}x + Q_{2n})^2}$$

and writes

$$\xi = T_n x = \frac{P_{2n}}{Q_{2n}} + \int_0^x \phi_n(t)dt.$$

Therefore the map T_n is *absolutely continuous*, i. e. the condition $\lambda(E) = 0$ implies $\lambda(T_n^{-1}E) = 0$ is satisfied. Then some measure theoretical devices are used. The set S_1 is contained in a set $\overline{S_1}$ which is the inner limiting set (this is the intersection) of a monotone decreasing sequence of a union of non-overlapping intervals such that $\lambda(\overline{S_1}) = \lambda(S_1)$. Let $\Sigma_1^{(n)} = T_n S_1$ and $\overline{\Sigma_1^{(n)}} = T_n \overline{S_1}$ then

$$\lambda(\Sigma_1^{(n)}) = \lambda(\overline{\Sigma_1^{(n)}}) = \int_{\overline{S_1}} \phi_n(x)dx = \int_0^1 f(x)\phi_n(x)dx$$

where $f(x)$ is the characteristic (= indicator) function of the set $\overline{S_1}$. Since $\phi_n(x)$ is continuous and $f(x)$ *summable* (= integrable) the first mean value theorem can be applied. It gives for a value $x_1 \in [0,1]$ the relation

$$\int_0^1 f(x)\phi_n(x)dx = \phi_n(x_1)\int_0^1 f(x)dx = \phi_n(x_1)\lambda(S_1).$$

Since S is invariant under the map T_n we find $\Sigma_1^{(n)} \subseteq S_1$. The density of S_1 in the interval $I^{(n)}$ is not less than the density of $\Sigma_1^{(n)}$ in this interval. Then

$$\frac{\lambda(I^{(n)} \cap S_1)}{\lambda(I^{(n)})} \geq \frac{\lambda(\Sigma_1^{(n)})}{\lambda(I^{(n)})} = \lambda(S_1)\frac{(Q_{2n-1} + Q_{2n})Q_{2n}}{(Q_{2n-1}x_1 + Q_{2n})^2} = \lambda(S_1)\frac{1+\theta}{1+\theta x_1}$$

where $\theta = \frac{Q_{2n-1}}{Q_{2n}} < 1$. Therefore

$$\liminf_n \frac{\lambda(I^{(n)} \cap S_1)}{\lambda(I^{(n)})} \geq \liminf_n \frac{\lambda(\Sigma_1^{(n)})}{\lambda(I^{(n)})} > 0.$$

Now Martin appeals to *Lebesgue's density theorem* which says that the density is either 1 or 0 at almost all points of a measurable set. This shows that $\lambda(S_1) = 1$.

Several conclusions follow, e. g. that the set of Liouville numbers or the set of Hurwitz numbers in the unit interval have measure 0 or 1. Now we know that they have measure 0.

Later [Ryll=Nardzewski 1951] simplifies Knopp's result. This important paper opened the road to apply ergodic theory to f-expansions and other parts of number theory. [Rényi 1957] followed this road. We illustrate his approach with continued fractions. Let $E = T^{-1}E$ and $\chi(x)$ its indicator function. If $B(c_1, ..., c_n) = \{x : b_1(x) = c_1, ..., b_n(x) = c_n\}$ is the interval with endpoints $\frac{p}{q}$ and $\frac{p'}{q'}$, $q' > q$, then

$$\lambda(E \cap B(c_1, ..., c_n)) = \int_0^1 \chi(y) \frac{dy}{(qy + q')^2} \geq \int_0^1 \chi(y) \frac{dy}{(q + q')^2}$$

$$\geq \frac{1}{4} \int_0^1 \chi(y) \frac{dy}{(q')^2} \geq \frac{1}{4} \lambda(E) \lambda(B(c_1, ..., c_n)).$$

Hence

$$\frac{\lambda(E \cap B(c_1, ..., c_n))}{\lambda(B(c_1, ..., c_n))} \geq \frac{\lambda(E)}{4}.$$

If $\lambda(E) > 0$ then the density of E must be 1.

For f-expansions with "independent digits" Rényi introduces

$$H_n(x, t) = \frac{d}{dt} f(\varepsilon_1(x) + f(\varepsilon_2(x) + ... + f(\varepsilon_n(x) + t)...))$$

and supposes

$$\sup_{0 < t < 1} H_n(x, t) \leq C \inf_{0 < t < 1} H_n(x, t).$$

For β-expansions which have "dependent digits" he has to modify the method. This argumentation is the origin of the *Rényi condition* (C). If (B, T) is a fibred system such that

1. $\lambda(B) = 1$

2. All cylinders are *full* (or *proper*), i. e. $TB(k) = B$ for all digits $k \in I$.

3. If the Jacobian functions $\omega(k_1, ..., k_s; x)$ are defined by

$$\int_A \omega(k_1, ..., k_s; x) dx = \int_{T^{-s}A \cap B(k_1, ..., k_s)} dx$$

then there is a constant $C \geq 1$ such that

$$\sup_{x \in B} \omega(k_1, ..., k_s; x) \leq C \inf_{x \in B} \omega(k_1, ..., k_s; x).$$

Since one works with the family of cylinders one needs a condition which ensures that the family of all cylinders generate the σ-algebra of Borel sets. A sufficient condition is that the diameters of cylinders converge to 0 as the rank n increases. For dimension $d = 1$ the diameter of an interval is just its length. The problems are more difficult for dimension $d \geq 2$.

Later several authors weakened Rényi's condition in several ways. We mention some concepts.

- *Finite range structure* The set of images $\{T^s B(k_1, ..., k_s)\}$ is finite (see e. g. [Ito & Yuri 1987]).

- *L-condition* There is a constant $L > 0$ such that all non-empty cylinders satisfy $\lambda(T^s B(k_1, ..., k_s)) \geq L$.

- *q-condition* There is a constant $q > 0$ such that any non-empty cylinder $B(k_1, ..., k_s)$ contains "sufficiently many" full cylinders such that

$$\sum_a \lambda(B(k_1, ..., k_s, a)) \geq q\lambda(B(k_1, ..., k_s)).$$

Sufficient conditions for the Rényi condition for f-expansions are given in [Adler 1973] . This theorem is now known as the "folklore theorem". These conditions are

1. T is twice continuously differentiable on each cylinder $B(k)$.

2. There exists an integer ν such that

$$\inf_{x \in B(k), k \in I} |\frac{d}{dx} T^\nu(x)| > 1.$$

3. $\sup_{x,y,z \in} |\frac{T''(x)}{T'(y)T'(z)}| < \infty$.

Adler explains that the second condition governs the expansiveness of the Map T (note that the identity map cannot be ergodic). The third condition says that T in some sense still is close to linearity (note that $T''(x) = 0$ if T is piecewise linear). For f-expansions it is sufficient to check the conditions

$$|f'(t)| \leq \eta \text{ for some } \eta < 1$$

and
$$\left|\frac{f''(t)}{f'(t)}\right| \text{ for some } M \geq 0.$$

The proof uses on the equation

$$\left|\log\frac{(T^n)'(x)}{(T^n)'(y)}\right| = \left|\int_x^y \frac{(T^n)'(z)}{(T^n)'(z)}dz\right|.$$

A detailled discussion of Adler's theorem and related questions can be found in [Halfant 1977].

Rényi's condition is in some sense reminiscent of Koebe's Distortion Theorem (see e. g. [Nevanlinna 1970]) which is related to an upper bound on the derivative of an injective map of the unit disk $\{z : |z| < 1\}$ onto another region.

Chapter 10

Rényi and further work on f-expansions

The present description of f-expansions was given in [Rényi 1957]. He distinguishes type A and type B. For type A he supposes that f is decreasing and satifies

(A1) $f(1) = 1$

(A2) The function f is positive, continuous and strictly decreasing for $1 \leq t \leq T$ and $\lim_{t \to T-0} f(t) = 0$. There are three subcases:

- (A2.1) $T = \infty$

- (A2.2) $2 < T < \infty$, T is an integer

- (A2.3) $1 < T < \infty$ and T is not an integer.

(A3)
$$|f(t) - f(s)| \leq |t - s|$$

for $1 \leq s < t$ and there is a constant λ such that $0 < \lambda < 1$ and

$$|f(t) - f(s)| \leq \lambda^2 |t - s|$$

if $1 + f(2) < s < t$. Rényi writes λ instead of λ^2 but since his proof of convergence closely follows Bissinger's method we write λ^2.

For type B f is increasing and satisfies

(B1) $f(0) = 0$

(B2) The function f is continuous and strictly increasing for $0 \leq t < T$ and $\lim_{t \to T-0} f(t) = 1$. There are again three subcases:

- (B2.1) $T = \infty$

- (B2.2) $2 \leq T < \infty$, T is an integer

- (B2.3) $1 < T < \infty$ and T is not an integer.

(B3)
$$|f(t) - f(s)| < |t - s|$$
for $0 \leq s < t$.

Rényi notes in a footnote that due to J. Czipszer condition (A3) could be replaced by a weaker condition.

We now suppose $0 < x < 1$. Rényi defines digits and an additional sequence by the recursion relations

$$r_0(x) = x, \; \epsilon_{n+1}(x) = \lfloor f^{-1}(r_n(x)) \rfloor, \; n \geq 0, \; r_{n+1}(x) = f^{-1}(r_n(x)) - \epsilon_{n+1}(x).$$

He defines

$$C_n(x) = f_n(\epsilon_1(x), \epsilon_2(x), ..., \epsilon_n(x)) = f(\epsilon_1 + f(\epsilon_2(x) + ... + f(\epsilon_n(x))...).$$

The proof for convergence of these f-expansions follows Everett's proof. For type B there is a modification. He introduces

$$D_n(x) = \liminf\{C_n(y) : C_n(y) > C_n(x)\}.$$

If the set on the right side is empty he puts $D_n(x) = 1$. Since f is increasing we see that
$$C_n(x) \leq x < D_n(x).$$

The sequence $(C_n(x))$ increases and the sequence $(D_n(x))$ decreases. Therefore

$$\underline{x} = \lim_{n \to \infty} C_n(x), \; \overline{x} = \lim_{n \to \infty} C_n(x)$$

both exist. Then
$$\epsilon_1(\overline{x}) = \epsilon_1(x) = \epsilon_1(\underline{x}).$$

If $\overline{x} - \underline{x} > 0$ then there exists a maximal "gap". Put $\underline{y} = r_1(\underline{x})$ and $\overline{y} = r_1(\overline{x})$ then

$$\overline{x} - \underline{x} = \frac{f(\epsilon_1(x) + \overline{y}) - f(\epsilon_1(x) + \underline{y})}{\overline{y} - \underline{y}}(\overline{y} - \underline{y}) < \overline{y} - \underline{y},$$

a contradiction.

A finite sequence $(\epsilon_1, \epsilon_2, ..., \epsilon_n)$ is called *canonical* if there is a number x such that $\epsilon_k(x) = \epsilon_k, 1 \leq k \leq n$. In cases (A2.1) and (A2.2) every sequence of digits with $1 \leq \epsilon_j < T$, $j = 1, 2, ..., n$ is canonical. In cases (B2.1) and (B2.2) the same applies if $0 \leq \epsilon_j < T$. Rényi uses the terminology *f-expansions with independent digits* although he remarks that could be misleading from the viewpoint of probability theory. Cases (A2.3) and (B2.3) are called *f-expansions with dependent digits*. We will illustrate this setting with β-expansions later. We now list some examples

(1) $f(x) = \frac{x}{q}$, $0 \leq x \leq q$, $q \geq 2$ is an integer. This is the well known decimal expansion with base q.

(2) $f(x) = \frac{1}{x}$ gives the regular continued fractions.

(3) $f(x) = \sqrt[m]{1+x} - 1$, $0 \leq x \leq 2^m - 1$, $m \geq 2$ is an integer. For $m = 2$ this was used by W. Bolyai in [Bolyai 1832].

(4) $f(x) = \frac{x}{\beta}$, $\beta = \frac{1+\sqrt{5}}{2}$ (the number of the *Golden Section*). This is a first example of the so-called *β-expansions*. The interval $[0, \frac{1}{\beta}[$ which corresponds to the digit $\epsilon_1(x) = 0$ is mapped under $Tx = \beta x$ onto $[0, 1[$. The interval $[\frac{1}{\beta}, 1[$ which corresponds to $\epsilon_1(x) = 1$ is mapped under $Tx = \beta x - 1$ onto $[0, \beta - 1[= [0, \frac{1}{\beta}[$. Therefore if $\epsilon_n(x) = 1$ then $\epsilon_{n+1}(x) = 0$. The sequence 11 is not admissible (or as Rényi says, not canonical)! This explains the notion of "dependent digits".

In the paper [Parry 1964b] the following class of functions is considered. Let $[a_i, b_i[\subseteq [i, i+1[$, $i = 0, 1, ..., k$ be a family of $k + 1$ intervals such that

$$D = \bigcup_{i=0}^{k} [a_i - i, b_i - i[= [0, 1[.$$

Let $f : D \to [0, 1[$ be a strictly increasing function. Then define as expected

$$Tx = f^{-1}x - \lfloor f^{-1}x \rfloor.$$

Parry speaks of a *representation process* generated by f. The unique monotonic extension of f to the domain $[0, \infty[$ and range $[0, 1[$ is denoted by $\overline{f}$. The process is called *valid* when every $x \in [0, 1[$ has a representation

$$x = \overline{f}(x_0 + \overline{f}(x_1 + ...))$$

where $x_n = \lfloor f^{-1}(T^n x) \rfloor$ for $n = 0, 1, 2, ...$. If one puts

$$\rho_n(x) = \overline{f}(x_0 + \overline{f}(x_1 + ... + \overline{f}(x_n)))$$

this means $x = \lim_{n \to \infty} \rho_n(x)$.

The first theorem says that f-expansions are valid if and only if $x \neq y$ implies

$x_i \neq y_i$ for all $i \geq 0$.
Next the *negative orbit* of the point x is defined as

$$\mathcal{O}^-(x) = \{y : T^n y = x \text{ for some } n \geq 0\}.$$

A map T is called *topologically transitive* if for an $x \in [0, 1[$ the orbit $\mathcal{O}^-(x)$ is dense in $[0, 1]$. Then, a necessary and sufficient condition for f-expansions to be valid is that $\bigcup_{i=0}^{k} \mathcal{O}^-(\alpha_i)$ be dense in $[0, 1]$ where $0 = \alpha_0 < \alpha_1 < \dots < \alpha_{k+1} = 1$ is the time-1-partition defined by $x_0 = i$ for $x \in [\alpha_i, \alpha_{i+1}[$. Note that $\alpha_i = \overline{f}(i)$, $0 \leq i \leq k$. If f has an interval $[a, b[$ as its domain then a necessary and sufficient condition for validity is that $\mathcal{O}^-(0)$ is dense in the unit interval. This follows from the observation that in this case $\{\alpha_1, \alpha_2, ..., \alpha_k\} \subseteq T^{-1}0 =$. More general, topological transitivity is sufficient for validity.
A remarkable addition is the construction of a strictly increasing function f with valid f-expansion such that for some x even $f'(x) = \infty$ occurs. Take $Sx = 2x - \lfloor 2x \rfloor$ and a homeomorphism $\Phi : [0, 1] \to [0, 1]$ such that $\Phi(0) = 0$, $\Phi'(\frac{1}{4}) = \infty$, and $\Phi(x) = x$ for $\frac{1}{2} \leq x \leq 1$. Then $Tx = \Phi S \Phi^{-1}(x)$ has valid f-expansions but $f'(\frac{1}{2}) = \infty$. Note that

$$f(x) = \Phi(\frac{1}{2}\Phi^{-1}(x)) \text{ for } 0 \leq x < 1$$

$$f(x) = \Phi(\frac{1}{2}(\Phi^{-1}(x - 1) + 1)) \text{ for } 1 \leq x < 2.$$

The core of the paper is the investigation of

$$f(x) = \frac{x - \alpha}{\beta} \text{ for } \alpha \leq x < \alpha + \beta, \, 1 \leq \beta, \, 0 \leq \alpha < 1.$$

This gives the map

$$Tx = \beta x + \alpha - \lfloor \beta x + \alpha \rfloor.$$

For $\beta = 1$ f-expansions are valid if and only if the number α is irrational. If $\alpha = 0$ and $\beta > 1$ we are back to β-expansions. Therefore Parry now considers $\beta > 1$ and $0 < \alpha < 1$. Let $\beta^2 = \beta + 1$ (β is the number of the *Golden Section*) and $\alpha = \frac{3-\beta}{2}$ then one calculates

$$T^{-1}[\frac{\beta - 1}{2}, \frac{3 - \beta}{2}[= [\frac{1}{\beta^2}, \frac{1}{\beta}[$$

$$\frac{\beta - 1}{2} < \frac{1}{\beta^2} < \frac{1}{\beta} < \frac{3 - \beta}{2}.$$

This means that $E = [\frac{\beta-1}{2}, \frac{3-\beta}{2}[$ satisfies $T^{-1}E \subset E$ but $0 < \lambda(E) < 1$. The map T is not *strongly ergodic*. The map T does not admit a finite measure which is equivalent to Lebesgue measure. However, T is ergodic and there is an invariant measure with density h, namely

$$h(x) = 1, \ 0 \le x < \frac{1}{\beta^2}, \ \frac{\beta}{2} \le x < 1$$

$$h(x) = \frac{1}{\beta}, \ \frac{1}{\beta^2} \le x < \frac{\beta-1}{2}, \ \frac{3-\beta}{2} \le x < \frac{\beta}{2}$$

$$h(x) = 0, \ \frac{\beta-1}{2} \le x < \frac{3-\beta}{2}.$$

Let T be a map and h an integrable function then the set function

$$\nu(E) = \int_E h(x)dx$$

is called an invariant *signed measure* if

$$h(x) = \sum_{n \ge 0} h(\overline{f}(x+n))\overline{f}'(x+n)$$

almost everywhere. A lengthy calculation shows that for

$$Tx = \beta x + \alpha - \lfloor \beta x + \alpha \rfloor$$

the function

$$h(x) = \sum_{x < T^n 1} \frac{1}{\beta^n} - \sum_{x < T^n 0} \frac{1}{\beta^n}$$

gives a signed measure. The problem remains to find out when $h(x) \ge 0$ almost everywhere.

The operator

$$Ag(x) = \sum_{0 \le \frac{x+m-\alpha}{\beta}} g\left(\frac{x+m-\alpha}{\beta}\right)\frac{1}{\beta}$$

is introduced. Clearly A is just the *transfer operator* for the map T (see the chapter Gauss, Kuzmin, and their followers). Note that

$$\int_{T^{-1}E} g d\lambda = \int_E Ag d\lambda.$$

Now one writes

$$h(x) = h^+(x) - h^-(x), \ h^+(x) = \max(h(x), 0), \ h^-(x) = \max(-h(x), 0).$$

Then we find $Ah^+(x) \geq h(x)$ and $h^-(x) \geq -h(x)$. Therefore $Ah^+ \geq h^+$ and $Ah^- \geq h^-$. Since

$$\int_0^1 Ah^+ d\lambda = \int_0^1 h^+ d\lambda$$

$$\int_0^1 Ah^- d\lambda = \int_0^1 h^- d\lambda$$

we see that $Ah^+ = h^+$ and $Ah^- = h^-$. Let $E = \{x : h^+(x) = 0\}$ then

$$\int_E h^+ d\lambda = \int_{T^{-1}E} h^+ d\lambda = 0.$$

This result implies $\lambda(T^{-1}E \setminus E) = 0$. If T is strongly ergodic $\lambda(E) = 0$ and $h^+ > 0$ almost everywhere. Then $\nu(E) = \int_E h^+ d\lambda$ is an invariant measure. Then, the ergodic theorem can be applied to strongly ergodic maps $Tx = \beta x + \alpha - \lfloor \beta x + \alpha \rfloor$ to compute frequency of digits.

[Rudolfer 1971] uses a slightly different definition for f-expansions but this is of no great importance. In the first part he studies some generalizations concerning ergodicity and convergence (following Rényi he speaks of *valid* expansions). The second part is devoted to two classes of maps. The first family is given by

$$f(x) = \frac{x}{b + cx}$$

which leads to the map

$$Tx = \frac{bx}{1 - cx} - \lfloor \frac{bx}{1 - cx} \rfloor.$$

To obtain an increasing function which produces at least two digits one has the conditions

$$b > 0, \quad \frac{b}{1 - c} > 1.$$

Under the conditions

$$b \geq 1, \, 1 - \sqrt{b} \leq c \leq 1$$

these f-expansions are valid which means that each $x \in [0, 1[$ has a unique f-expansion. If $\frac{b}{1-c} \geq 2$ is an integer then T is *ergodic*. If $b > 1$ and $0 < c \leq 1$ then there exist an *invariant measure* equivalent to λ. Only for $c = 1$ the density is given, namely

$$h(x) = \frac{b}{b - 1 + x}.$$

If $b = 1$ the measure is infinite but the map

$$Tx = \frac{1}{1-x} \quad \text{mod } 1$$

is conservative. The method of dual algorithm would show that for $0 < c < 1$ the density is given as

$$h(x) = \frac{c}{b-1+cx} - \frac{c-c^2}{b-1+2c-c^2x}.$$

The second family is given by

$$f(x) = \frac{1}{ax+b}.$$

It is proved that for $a > 0$ and $0 \le b \le 1$ the associated f-expansion is valid. The corresponding map is

$$Tx = \frac{1-(aj+b)x}{ax}, \, j \ge j_0 = \lfloor \frac{1-b}{a} \rfloor.$$

Rudolfer mentions the following special cases
(i) $a > 0$, $b = 1$ with the map

$$Tx = \frac{1-x}{ax} - j, \, j \ge j_0 = 0.$$

(ii) $b = 0$, $a = \frac{1}{N}$. The map

$$Tx = \frac{N}{x} - j, \, j \ge j_0 = N$$

is useful in connection with the *Hausdorff dimension* of the set of all numbers with $a_j(x) \ge N$ in their regular continued fraction expansion.
In both cases the invariant density is given by the function

$$h(x) = \frac{1}{ax+1}.$$

However, it easy to see that there are many more cases for which the invariant density can be determined. Take $a = \frac{1}{5}$ and $b = \frac{3}{5}$, i. e. $f(x) = \frac{5}{3+x}$ then the invariant density is

$$h(x) = \frac{1}{5+x}.$$

[Roos 1965] uses the concept „Resttransformation" for the map T which is related to the f-expansions considered in his paper.

Chapter 11

Gauss, Kuzmin, and their followers

Let

$$\alpha = \cfrac{1}{a_1 + \cfrac{1}{a_2 + \dots}}$$

be an infinite continued fraction and then denote

$$T^n\alpha = \cfrac{1}{a_{n+1} + \cfrac{1}{a_{n+2} + \dots}}.$$

We put

$$m_n(x) = \lambda(\{\alpha : T^{n+1}\alpha < x\}).$$

In the year 1812 Carl Friedrich Gauss stated in a letter to Pierre Simon de Laplace that he found

$$\lim_{n\to\infty} m_n(x) = \frac{\log(1+x)}{\log 2}.$$

Gauss pointed out that it would be desirable to obtain an estimate for the difference

$$m_n(x) - \frac{\log(1+x)}{\log 2}.$$

Let us present Gauss' words. Note that Gauss used $P(n,x) = m_n(x)$ and he did not use a symbol for the limit «Cependant j'ai trouvé par des raisonnements tres simples que pour n infini on a

$$P(n,x) = \frac{\log(1+x)}{\log 2}.$$

Mais les efforts que j'ai fait lors de mes recherches pour assigner

$$P(n,x) - \frac{\log(1+x)}{\log 2}$$

pour une valeur tres grande de n, mais pas infinie, ont été infructueux.»[Gauss 1812].

Maybe, Gauss knew that the sequence $m_0(x), m_1(x), m_2(x), \ldots$ satisfies the functional equation

$$m_{n+1}(x) = \sum_{k=1}^{\infty} \left(m_n(\frac{1}{k}) - m_n(\frac{1}{k+1}) \right).$$

In fact, this is easy to see. If

$$T^n \alpha = \frac{1}{a_{n+1} + T^{n+1}\alpha}$$

then

$$T^{n+1}\alpha < x$$

is equivalent to

$$\frac{1}{a_{n+1} + x} < T^n\alpha \le \frac{1}{a_{n+1}}.$$

On the other hand the function $\phi(x) = \log(1+x)$ is a solution of this functional equation.

If we put $m'_n(x) = f_n(x)$ then the functions f_n satisfy the functional equation

$$f_{n+1}(x) = \sum_{k=1}^{\infty} f_n\left(\frac{1}{k+x}\right) \frac{1}{(k+x)^2},$$

the so-called *Kuzmin equation*.

Kuzmin proved the following result [Kuzmin 1928]. Let $f_0(x), f_1(x), f_2(x), \ldots$ be a sequence of real functions on the interval $[0,1]$ such that

$$0 < m < f_0(x) < M, \ |f'_0(x)| < \mu$$

for some constants m, M, μ and

$$f_{n+1}(x) = \sum_{k=1}^{\infty} f_n\left(\frac{1}{k+x}\right)\frac{1}{(k+x)^2}$$

then

$$f_n(x) = \frac{a}{1+x} + Ae^{-\lambda\sqrt{n}}$$

where

$$a = \frac{1}{\log 2}\int_0^1 f_0(x)dx, \ \lambda > 0, \ A = A(M,\mu) > 0.$$

From the viewpoint of *ergodic theory* this result means that the sequence $f_n(x)$ converges to the invariant density.
We sketch the proof of this important result. The functional relation implies

$$f_n(x) = \sum f_0\left(\frac{p_n + p_{n-1}x}{q_n + q_{n-1}x}\right)\frac{1}{(q_n + q_{n-1}x)^2}.$$

The sum runs over all admissible blocks $(a_1, a_2, ..., a_n)$. This relation implies

$$f'_n(x) = \sum f'_0\left(\frac{p_n + p_{n-1}x}{q_n + q_{n-1}x}\right)\frac{(-1)^n}{(q_n + q_{n-1})^4} - 2\sum f_0\left(\frac{p_n + p_{n-1}x}{q_n + q_{n-1}x}\right)\frac{q_{n-1}}{(q_n + q_{n-1})^2}.$$

From

$$\frac{1}{(q_n + q_{n-1}x)^2} < \frac{2}{q_n(q_n + q_{n-1})}$$

and

$$q_n(q_n + q_{n-1}) > 2^{n-1}$$

we get

$$|f'_n(x)| < \frac{\mu}{2^{n+3}} + 4M < 5M,$$

if n is large enough.
It is easy to see that

$$\frac{t}{1+x} < f_n(x) < \frac{T}{1+x}$$

implies

$$\frac{t}{1+x} < f_{n+1}(x) < \frac{T}{1+x}.$$

Last but not least we remark that

$$\int_0^1 f_n(z)dz = \int_0^1 f_0(z)dz.$$

The proof starts after these preliminaries! With $g = \frac{m}{2}$ and $G = 2M$ we obtain

$$\frac{g}{1+x} < f_0(x) < \frac{G}{1+x}.$$

The sequence

$$\phi_n(x) = f_n(x) - \frac{g}{1+x}$$

also satisfies the Kuzmin equation. An essential idea is to compare the integral $\int_0^1 \phi_0(z)dz$ with

$$\phi_n(x) = \sum \phi_0\Big(\frac{p_n + p_{n-1}x}{q_n + q_{n-1}x}\Big) \frac{1}{(q_n + q_{n-1}x)^2}.$$

We see that

$$\phi_n(x) > \frac{1}{2}\sum \phi_0\Big(\frac{p_n + p_{n-1}x}{q_n + q_{n-1}x}\Big) \frac{1}{q_n(q_n + q_{n-1})}$$

but by applying the mean value theorem we obtain

$$\frac{1}{2}\int_0^1 \phi_0(z)dz = \frac{1}{2}\sum \phi_0(\xi) \frac{1}{q_n(q_n + q_{n-1})}$$

where ξ lies between $\frac{p_n}{q_n}$ and $\frac{p_n+p_{n-1}}{q_n+q_{n-1}}$. Then

$$\phi_n(x) - \frac{1}{2}\int_0^1 \phi_0(z)dz > \frac{1}{2}\sum \Big(\phi_0\Big(\frac{p_n + p_{n-1}x}{q_n + q_{n-1}x}\Big) - \phi_0(\xi)\frac{1}{q_n(q_n + q_{n-1})}\Big).$$

Since

$$|\phi_0'(x)| \le |f_0'(x)| + g < \mu + g$$

we have

$$\Big|\phi_0\Big(\frac{p_n + p_{n-1}x}{q_n + q_{n-1}x}\Big) - \phi_0(\xi)\Big| < \frac{\mu + g}{q_n(q_n + q_{n-1})} < \frac{\mu + g}{2^{n-1}}.$$

This result shows

$$\phi_n(x) > \frac{1}{2}\int_0^1 \phi_0(z)dz - \frac{\mu + g}{2^n}$$

and

$$f_n(x) > \frac{g}{1+x} + \frac{1}{2}\int_0^1 \phi_0(z)dz - \frac{\mu + g}{2^n}$$

$$= \frac{1}{1+x}\Big(g + \frac{1+x}{2}\int_0^1 \phi_0(z)dz - \frac{(1+x)(\mu + g)}{2^n}\Big).$$

Since $1 \leq 1 + x \leq 2$ we finally get

$$f_n(x) > \frac{1}{1+x}\left(g + \frac{1}{2}\int_0^1 \phi_0(z)dz - \frac{\mu+g}{2^{n-1}}\right) = \frac{g_1}{1+x}.$$

If n is sufficiently large then $g < g_1$.
In a similar way we consider the sequence

$$\psi_n(x) = \frac{G}{1+x} - f_n(x)$$

and obtain

$$f_n(x) < \frac{G_1}{1+x}.$$

Again for sufficiently large n we have $G_1 < G$.
Since

$$\frac{1}{2}\left(\int_0^1 \phi_0(z)dz + \int_0^1 \psi_0(z)dz\right) = \frac{1}{2}\int_0^1 \frac{G-g}{1+z}dz = \frac{\log 2}{2}(G-g)$$

we obtain

$$G_1 - g_1 < (G-g)\delta + 2^{-n+2}(\mu+G), \ \delta = \frac{\log 2}{2}.$$

Kuzmin and also Khintchine admit a slight error. They say that taking not $f_0(x)$ but $f_n(x)$ the repetition of the previous reasoning would let them arrive at the inequality

$$\frac{g_2}{1+x} < f_{2n}(x) < \frac{G_2}{1+x}$$

with

$$g_1 < g_2 < G_2 < G_1$$

and

$$G_2 - g_2 < (G_1 - g_1)\delta + \frac{5M}{2^{n-2}} + g_1).$$

They replace $\phi_0(x)$ by the new function $\phi_n(x)$ but then

$$\int_0^1 \phi_n(z)dz < \int_0^1 \phi_0(z)dz.$$

It is not clear that the same value of n makes

$$g_2 = g_1 + \frac{1}{2}\int_0^1 \phi_n(z)dz - \frac{5M+g_1}{2^{n-1}} > g_1.$$

Therefore one cannot replace n by $2n$ at this step. A possible repair follows. We see that

$$g_1 = g\delta + \beta_n, \text{ with } \beta_n = \frac{1}{2}\int_0^1 f_0(z)dz - \frac{5M + g}{2^{n-1}}$$

and

$$G_1 = G\delta + \gamma_n, \text{ with } \gamma_n = \frac{1}{2}\int_0^1 f_0(z)dz + \frac{5M + g}{2^{n-1}}$$

which again gives

$$G_1 - g_1 < (G - g)\delta + \frac{5M + G}{2^{n-2}}.$$

Then by substituting $\phi_0(x) = f_0(x) - \frac{g}{1+x}$ and $\phi_n(x) = f_n(x) - \frac{g_1}{1+x}$ we arrive at

$$g_2 = g_1\delta + \beta_n = g_2\delta^2 + \beta_n(1 + \delta).$$

Then

$$g_n = g\delta^n + \beta_n(1 + \delta + ... + \delta^{n-1})$$

and similarly

$$G_n = G\delta^n + \gamma_n(1 + \delta + ... + \delta^{n-1}).$$

Since

$$G_n - g_n < (G - g)\delta^n + \frac{5M + G}{2^{n-2}}$$

we see that

$$\lim_{n\to\infty} g_n = \lim_{n\to\infty} G_n = \frac{1}{\log 2}\int_0^1 f_0(z)dz.$$

But note that replacing n by n^2 we obtain our result.

Another approach to the problem of Gauss was done in [Lévy 1929] which we present in another chapter. An important step was made in [Doeblin 1940]. He uses the theory of *chains with complete connections* («chaînes à liaisons complètes») which seems to be introduced in [Onicescu & Mihoc 1935](see also [Doeblin & Fortet 1937]). Unfortunately the paper is hard to read which may be one of the reasons that this approach has not been followed so often. Nevertheless, Doeblin influenced the development of probability theory as the book [Cohn 1993] shows. In this collection there are papers which are closely connected to our subject. The Romanian school (see e. g. the monograph [Iosifescu and Grigorescu 1990]) used it extensively and also in connection with f-expansions (see also [Kalpazidou 1985]). An important step is hidden in a footnote. If

$$y = \cfrac{1}{b_1 + \cfrac{1}{b_2 + \dots}}$$

and $y_r = \frac{p_r}{q_r}$ then with constants θ and $0 < \rho < 1$ we have

$$|y - y_r| < \theta \rho^r$$

but with another constant $\bar{\theta}$ also

$$\frac{y+1}{yx+1} - \frac{y_r+1}{y_r x+1} = \frac{y_r+1}{y_r x+1}(1 + \bar{\theta}\rho^r).$$

Doeblin uses the invariant measure for continued fractions on $[1, \infty[$, namely for the map

$$Sx = \frac{1}{x-k} = x_1, \ k < x \le k+1.$$

Its density is given as

$$h(x) = \frac{1}{x(1+x)}.$$

He obtains a convergence rate in the form $Ke^{-\lambda\sqrt{n}}$ but he says that Fortet using analytic methods gets Lévy's rate $Ke^{-\lambda n}$ ([Doeblin 1940:357]). Doeblin also mentions a *central limit theorem* and a *law of iterated logarithm*. If

$$S^n(x) = \sum_{i=1}^{n} f(a_i)$$

and

$$M = \frac{1}{\log 2} \sum_{p=1}^{\infty} \log \frac{(p+1)^2}{p(p+2)}$$

then the measure of points $x \in [0, 1]$ which satisfy the inequality

$$z_1 \sigma \sqrt{n} < S^n(x) - nM < z_2 \sigma \sqrt{n}$$

is given by

$$\frac{1}{\sqrt{2\pi}} \int_{z_1}^{z_2} e^{-\frac{z^2}{2}} dz + O(n^{-\delta})$$

for a $\delta > 0$. Further, for almost all x and $c > \frac{3}{2}$ there is an $n(x, c)$ such that

$$|S^n(x) - nM| < \sqrt{2\sigma^2 n(\log_2 n + c \log_3 n)}.$$

If $c \le \frac{1}{2}$ then for almost all x there are infinitely many values of n such that

$$|S^n(x) - nM| \ge \sqrt{2\sigma^2 n(\log_2 n + c\log_3 n)}.$$

The proofs can be found in [Doeblin 1937]. He also remarks that $\sigma = 0$ only appears in the case $f(p) = $ constant.

In connection with the calculation of several mean values he also gives a passing notice to the ergodic theorem («Il résulte du théorème connu de Birkhoff-Khintchine ... », [Doeblin 1940:366]).

The last chapter in his paper is devoted to *Poisson's law*. The proof is incomplete (see [Iosifescu 1977]). We mention one result If

$$S_n = a_1 + a_2 + \dots + a_n$$

then the series

$$\sum_{n=1}^{\infty} \left(\frac{1}{S_n} - \frac{\log 2}{n\log n}\right)$$

converges absolutely for almost all x.

Now it is time to introduce the *transfer operator* (also named *Kuzmin operator* or *Frobenius-Perron operator*). Let $T : B \to B$ be a *non-singular* map (which means that $\lambda(E) = 0$ implies $\lambda(T^{-1}E) = 0$) then for any integrable function f the transfer operator A is defined by the equation

$$\int_{T^{-1}E} f d\lambda = \int_E (Af)d\lambda$$

for any measurable set E. We note that the definition of A can be extended to measurable non-negative functions.

Why is Af well defined? If f is integrable then

$$\nu(E) = \int_{T^{-1}E} f d\lambda$$

is a *signed measure*. Since T is non-singular the condition $\lambda(E) = 0$ implies $\nu(E) = 0$. Then the famous theorem of Radon-Nikodym which can be found in almost all books on measure theory ensures that there is an integrable function g such that

$$\nu(E) = \int_E g d\lambda.$$

This function g is denoted as Af. It is easy to see that A is a linear operator and A is positive which means that $f \ge 0$ implies $Af \ge 0$. Furthermore

$$\int_B f d\lambda = \int_B (Af)d\lambda.$$

If (B, T) is a fibred system then

$$T^{-1}E = \bigcup_{k \in I} V(k)E.$$

Then the equality

$$\int_{T^{-1}E} f d\lambda = \sum_{k \in I} \int_{V(k)E} f d\lambda = \sum_{k \in I} \int_B (f \circ V(k)) \omega(k) d\lambda$$

$$= \int_B \Big(\sum_{k \in I} (f \circ V(k)) \omega(k) \Big) d\lambda$$

shows

$$(Af)(x) = \sum_{k \in I} f(V(k)x) \omega(k; x),$$

the (generalized) Kuzmin equation.

It is clear that a function h is the density of an invariant measure if and only if $Ah = h$.

If we take a start function $f_0(x)$ we look at the iteration

$$f_{n+1}(x) = \sum_{k \in I} f_n(V(k)x) \omega(k; x).$$

Using the transfer operator we write

$$f_{n+1} = A f_n = A^{n+1} f_0.$$

Since A is a positive linear operator clearly methods of *functional analysis* can be applied to the Gauss problem, namely to determine estimates for $f_n(x) - h(x)$. The speed of convergence depends on the choice of the space of functions under consideration. For continued fractions this is discussed in considerable detail in [Iosifescu & Kraaikamp 2002]. The historical development of the metrical theory of continued fractions is also sketched in [Rieger 1977].

Another remarkable proof for Lipschitz functions is given in [Iosifescu 1994]. We denote by

$$s(f) = \sup_{x < y} \Big| \frac{f(x) - f(y)}{x - y} \Big|$$

and we use the transfer operator U with respect to the invariant measure, i. e.

$$\int_E (Uf) d\mu = \int_{T^{-1}E} f d\mu.$$

The norm in this Banach space is given as

$$||f|| = ||f||_\infty + s(f).$$

The proof relies on the estimate

$$s(Uf) \le (2\zeta(3) - \zeta(2))s(f).$$

The constant $2\zeta(3) - \zeta(2)$ is best possible. Take $f(x) = x$ then $s(f) = 1$ and

$$(Uf)(x) = \sum_{k=1}^\infty \frac{x+1}{(x+k)^2(x+k+1)} = g(x).$$

Then

$$|g'(0)| = \sum_{k=1}^\infty \frac{k^2 - 2k - 2}{k^3(k+1)^2}$$

$$= \sum_{k=1}^\infty \left(\frac{2}{k^3} - \frac{2}{k^2} + \frac{1}{k} - \frac{1}{k+1} + \frac{1}{(k+1)^2} \right) = 2\zeta(3) - \zeta(2).$$

[Tran Vinh-Hien 1963] considers f-expansions defined on $[1, S]$ or $[0, S]$ where S is an integer or $S = \infty$. He closely follows Rényi's paper [Rényi 1957] and uses two additional assumptions

1. $\sum_{(\varepsilon_1, ..., \varepsilon_n)} |f''(\varepsilon_1, ..., \varepsilon_n; x)| < C_1$ for a constant $C_1 > 0$.

2. The invariant density h is differentiable and satisfies $|h'(x)| < N$ for a constant $N > 0$.

Define

$$\Psi_{n+1}(x) = \sum_k f'(x+k)|\Psi_n(f(x+k))|$$

for a differentiable start function $\Psi_0(x)$ which satisfies $0 < \Psi_0(x) < M$ and $|\Psi_0'(x)| < \beta$. Then he states a convergence result for $\Psi_n(x)$ in the form

$$\Psi_n(x) = h(x) \int_0^1 \Psi_0(x)dx + \theta A e^{-\xi\sqrt{n}}$$

with constants $A > 0$, $\xi > 0$.
He then considers the functions

$$M_n(x) = \mu\{t : a_1(t) = i_1, ..., a_k(t) = i_k, T^{n+k}t < x\}$$

and

$$\chi_n(x) = \frac{M_n(x)}{\mu(B(i_1, ..., i_n))}$$

and deduces the *mixing property*

$$|\mu(B(i_1, ..., i_k) \cap T^{-k-n} B(j_1, ..., j_s) - \mu(B(i_1, ..., i_k))\mu(B(j_1, ..., j_s)))|$$

$$< Ae^{-\xi\sqrt{n}} \mu(B(i_1, ..., i_k))\mu(B(j_1, ..., j_s)).$$

This leads to a *central limit theorem* for certain functions $g \in L_2$ with

$$\int_0^1 g(t)d\mu(t) = 0,$$

namely

$$\mu\{t : \frac{g(t) + ... + g(T^{n-1}t)}{\sigma\sqrt{n}} < z\} \to \frac{1}{2\pi} \int_{-\infty}^z e^{-\frac{w^2}{2}} dw$$

for $n \to \infty$.

[Rieger 1978] extends the theorem of Kuzmin to continued fractions to the nearest integer. This is a continued fraction of the type

$$x = k_0 + \cfrac{\varepsilon_1}{k_1 + \cfrac{\varepsilon_2}{k_2 + ...}}$$

characterized by the conditions $k_0 \in \mathbb{Z}$, $k_j \in \mathbb{N}$ and $k_j \geq 2$, $\varepsilon_j \in \{1, -1\}$, $k_j + \varepsilon_{j+1} \geq 2$ for $j \geq 1$. Rieger does not mention ergodic theory or invariant measures. He introduces the map

$$S\xi = \frac{1}{|\xi|} - \lfloor \frac{1}{|\xi|} + \frac{1}{2} \rfloor = \frac{\varepsilon_1(\xi)}{\xi} - k_1(\xi)$$

for $-\frac{1}{2} < \xi < \frac{1}{2}$, $\xi \neq 0$ and the functions

$$H_n(\alpha) = \lambda\{\xi : 0 \leq S^n\xi \leq \alpha\}, 0 \leq \alpha \leq \frac{1}{2}$$

$$H_n(\alpha) = \lambda\{\xi : 0 \leq S^n\xi \leq \frac{1}{2} \text{ or } -\frac{1}{2} \leq S^n\xi \leq \alpha - 1\}, \frac{1}{2} < \alpha \leq 1$$

starting with $H_0(\alpha) = \alpha$. This sequence satisfies the recursion relation

$$H_{n+1}(\alpha) = \sum_{k \geq 2} \left(H_n(\frac{1}{k}) - H_n(\frac{1}{k+\alpha}) + H_n(1 - \frac{1}{k+\alpha}) - H_n(1 - \frac{1}{k})\right).$$

If $H(\alpha) = \lim_{n \to \infty} H_n(\alpha)$ exists then the function H clearly satisfies the functional equation

$$H(\alpha) = \sum_{k \geq 2} \left(H(\frac{1}{k}) - H(\frac{1}{k+\alpha}) + H(1 - \frac{1}{k+\alpha}) - H(1 - \frac{1}{k}) \right).$$

It is easy to verify that

$$H(\alpha) = \frac{1}{\log G} \log \frac{G+\alpha}{G}, \ G^2 = G + 1, \ G > 1$$

is a solution. Following his predecessors Rieger investigates the convergence behavior of the derivatives. He introduces the sequence

$$\gamma_{n+1}(\alpha) = \sum_{k \geq 2} \left(\gamma_n(\frac{1}{k+\alpha}) \frac{\alpha + G}{G(\alpha + G + k - 1)(\alpha + k)} \right)$$

$$+ \gamma_n \left(1 - \frac{1}{k+\alpha} \right) \frac{\alpha + G}{(G+1)(\alpha + G + k - 2)(\alpha + k)} \right)$$

with a start function γ_0 which is continuously differentiable on $0 \leq \alpha \leq 1$. Without making it explicit this means to replace the transfer operator with respect to Lebesgue measure by the transfer operator with respect to the equivalent invariant measure. A lot of cumbersome calculations show

$$|\gamma_n(\alpha) - \gamma_n(0)| \leq \sup_{0 \leq \alpha \leq 1} |\gamma_n'(\alpha)| (\frac{3}{4})^n.$$

This implies

$$H_n(\alpha) = \frac{1}{\log G} \log \frac{G+\alpha}{G} + O((\frac{3}{4})^n).$$

Rieger remarks that the constant $\frac{3}{4}$ is far from optimal but Wirsing's method [Wirsing 1974] cannot be easily transferred (we will return to this paper in the sequel) .

Now, the density of the invariant probability measure is given as

$$g(x) = \frac{1}{(\log(G+1) - \log G)(G + x)}, \ x > 0$$

$$g(x) = \frac{1}{(\log(G+1) - \log G)(G + 1 + x)}, \ x < 0.$$

Its distribution function therefore is

$$G(x) = \int_{-\frac{1}{2}}^{x} g(t) dt.$$

The connection to Rieger's function H is the following

$$H(1)G(x) = H(x) + H(1) - H(\frac{1}{2}), \text{ if } 0 \leq x \leq \frac{1}{2}$$

$$H(1)G(x) = H(x+1) - H(\frac{1}{2}), \text{ if } -\frac{1}{2} \leq x \leq 0.$$

Rieger's choice of H instead of G avoids the distinction for the transfer operator, namely if $k_1(x) = 2$ then $\varepsilon_2(x) = 1$ must follow.
Rieger also mentions *singular continued fractions*

$$x = k_0 + \cfrac{\varepsilon_1}{k_1 + \cfrac{\varepsilon_2}{k_2 + ...}}$$

with the conditions $k_0 \in \mathbb{Z}$, $\varepsilon_j \in \{-1, 1\}$, $k_j \geq 2$ and $k_j + \varepsilon_j \geq 2$ for all $j \geq 1$ and he states similar results. Both continued fractions are special cases of the so-called *Japanese continued fractions* of type I. Let $\frac{1}{2} \leq \alpha \leq 1$ fixed then the associated fibred system on $[\alpha - 1, \alpha]$ is given by

$$Tx = |\frac{1}{x}| - \lfloor |\frac{1}{x}| + 1 - \alpha \rfloor, x \neq 0.$$

The case $\alpha = \frac{1}{2}$ gives continued fractions to the nearest integer, the case $\alpha = \frac{\sqrt{5}-1}{2}$ singular continued fractions.
The quality of approximation in a Kuzmin type theorem depends on the chosen space of functions. [Iosifescu 1992] presents a simple proof for the space $BV([0,1])$, the *Banach space* of complex valued functions $f : [0,1] \to \mathbb{C}$ of bounded variation with the norm

$$||f|| = \mathrm{var}f + ||f||_\infty.$$

Remember that $\mathrm{var}f = \sup \sum_{i=1}^{k-1} |f(t_i) - f(t_{i+1})|$ with $0 \leq t_1 < t_2 < ... < t_k \leq 1$. Let

$$(Uf)(x) = \sum_{k=1}^{\infty} f\left(\frac{1}{x+k}\right) \frac{x+1}{(x+k)(x+k+1)}$$

be the transfer operator with respect to the invariant measure. Then the first result is

$$\mathrm{var}Uf \leq \frac{1}{2}\mathrm{var}f + (6 - 4\sqrt{2})|f|.$$

If

$$p_k(x) = \frac{x+1}{(x+k)(x+k+1)}$$

then
$$p'_k(x) = \frac{k-1}{(x+k)^2} - \frac{k}{(x+k+1)^2}.$$

Therefore
$$p'_1(x) < 0$$
$$p'_2(x) < 0, \text{ if } x \in [0, \sqrt{2}-1[$$
$$p'_2(x) > 0, \text{ if } x \in]\sqrt{2}-1, 1]$$
$$p'_k(x) > 0, \text{ if } k \geq 3.$$

Hence we see
$$\|p_1\|_\infty = \frac{1}{2}, \ \|p_2\|_\infty = 3 - \sqrt{2}, \ \|p_k\|_\infty = \frac{2}{(k+1)(k+2)}, \ k \geq 3.$$

Some calculations show
$$\sum_{k=1}^\infty \mathrm{var} p_k = 6 - 4\sqrt{2}.$$

Let $w_k(x) = \frac{1}{k+x}$ then

$$\mathrm{var} Uf = \mathrm{var} \sum_k p_k \cdot f \circ w_k \leq \sum_k \mathrm{var}(p_k \cdot f \circ w_k)$$

$$\leq \sum_k \|p_k\|_\infty \mathrm{var}(f \circ w_k) + \sum_k \|f \circ w_k\|_\infty \mathrm{var} p_k$$

$$\leq \frac{1}{2} \sum_k \mathrm{var}_{[\frac{1}{k+1}, \frac{1}{k}]} f + \|f\|_\infty \mathrm{var} p_k \leq \frac{1}{2} \mathrm{var} f + (6 - \sqrt{2})\|f\|_\infty.$$

If
$$U^\infty = \frac{1}{2} \int_0^1 \frac{f(x)}{1+x} dx$$

then one can deduce from this result the existence of a constant $0 < \theta < 1$ (Iosifescu gives $\theta = 0.84314...$) such that

$$\|U^n f - U^\infty f\| \leq 2\theta^n \|f\|.$$

We will present some more results on the *transfer operator* (also named *Kuzmin operator* or *Frobenius-Perron operator*). In their book on this operator the authors write "The hero of this book is the Frobenius-Perron operator"[Boyarski & Góra 1997:74]. We repeat its definition. Let $T : B \to B$ be a *non-singular* map (which means that $\lambda(E) = 0$ implies $\lambda(T^{-1}E) = 0$) then for any integrable function f the transfer operator A is defined by the equation

$$\int_{T^{-1}E} f d\lambda = \int_E (Af) d\lambda$$

for any measurable set E.

We first present Wirsing's approach to Kuzmin's equation for continued fractions [Wirsing 1974]. Let

$$m_n(x) = \lambda\{\alpha : T^{n+1}\alpha < x\}$$

and put

$$r_n(x) = m_n(x) - \frac{\log(1+x)}{\log 2}.$$

From the papers [Lévy 1929] and [Szüsz 1961] we know that there is a constant $0 < q < 1$ such that $r_n(x) = O(q^n)$. Lévy obtained $q \leq 0.7$ and Szüsz with some elaboration $q \leq \sqrt{(2\zeta(3) - \zeta(2))(7 + 2\zeta(4) - 6\zeta(3) - \zeta(2))}$.

Before he enters into operator theory Wirsing shows that there are constants $c_1, c_2 > 0$ such that

$$\frac{c_2}{5^n} x(1-x) \leq |r_n(x)| \leq \frac{c_1}{2^n} x(1-x).$$

He replaces the transfer operator A by the transfer operator B with respect to the invariant measure, namely

$$\int_{T^{-1}E} f d\mu = \int_E (Bf) d\mu.$$

Since the invariant measure is known we get the explicit form

$$(Bf)(x) = \sum_{k=1}^{\infty} \frac{1+x}{(k+x)(k+1+x)} f(\frac{1}{k+x}).$$

Then he introduces a new operator

$$(Ug)(x) = \sum_{k=1}^{\infty} \left(\frac{k}{(k+1+x)^2} \int_{\frac{1}{k+1+x}}^{\frac{1}{k+x}} g(y) dy + \frac{1+x}{(k+x)^3(k+1+x)} g(\frac{1}{k+x}) \right).$$

The origin of this operator is the equation

$$\frac{d}{dx}(Bf)(x) = -(Uf')(x).$$

Note that the operator U is positive, i. e. if $\phi_1 \leq \phi_2$ then $U\phi_1 \leq U\phi_2$. If one takes

$$f(x) = 1 + x - \frac{1}{1+x}$$

then

$$(Bf)(x) = 1 + \frac{1}{1+x}.$$

Therefore

$$\phi(x) = 1 + \frac{1}{(1+x)^2}$$

gives

$$(U\phi)(x) = \frac{1}{(1+x)^2}.$$

Then we obtain

$$\frac{1}{5}\phi \leq U\phi \leq \frac{1}{2}\phi.$$

From this inequality eventually the final estimate is derived. If one uses

$$\phi(x) = 1 + \frac{1}{(1+x)^2} + \frac{2}{(1+2x)^2}$$

then one could obtain

$$c_2(0.24528302)^n x(1-x) \leq |r_n(x)| \leq c_1(0.33190278)^n x(1-x).$$

The main goal of this paper is to prove that there are constants $0 < \mu < \lambda < 1$ and a real function Ψ such that

$$r_n(x) = (-\lambda)^n \Psi(x) + O(x(1-x)\mu^n).$$

Numerical computations give $\lambda = 0.3036630029....$ The function Ψ can be analytically continued in the region $\mathbb{C} \setminus \{z = x : -\infty < x \leq -1\}$ and satisfies the functional equation

$$\Psi(z) - \Psi(z+1) = \frac{1}{\lambda}\Psi\left(\frac{1}{z+1}\right).$$

Wirsing's work was continued by several authors (e. g. [Fluch 1986], [Babenko 1978], [Mayer & Roepstorff 1987, 1988]. A good exposition can be found in [Iosifescu & Kraaikamp 2002].

We mention two papers by Gordin. These papers appeared in the proceedings of the Soviet Academy of Sciences. They are short reports on results. The frame in [Gordin 1968] is the same as in [Rényi 1957]. He introduces the transfer operator V by the equation

$$\int_A (Vg)(x)dP(x) = \int_{T^{[-1}} g(x)dP(x)$$

on a measurable set. P refers to the invariant measure. He deals with functions of *bounded variation* and uses some assumptions on the functions

$$f(\varepsilon_1, \varepsilon_2, ..., \varepsilon_n; x) = f(\varepsilon_1 + f(\varepsilon_2 + ... + f(\varepsilon_n + x))).$$

If there is a constant $K > 0$ such that for all $n \geq 1$ the condition

$$\sum_{(\varepsilon_1, \varepsilon_2, ..., \varepsilon_n)} \text{var}(\frac{df(\varepsilon_1, \varepsilon_2, ..., \varepsilon_n; x)}{dx}) \leq K$$

is satisfied he claims that for a function f of bounded variation there are constants $A > 0$ and $\lambda > 0$ such that

$$\text{esssup}_{0<x<1}|(V^n g)(x) - \int_0^1 g(u)dP(u)| \leq Ae^{-\lambda n}\text{var}(g).$$

Unfortunately nothing is said about the proof and the size of the constant $e^{-\lambda}$. He remarks that the conditions of the theorem do not apply to $Tx = \theta x - \lfloor \theta x \rfloor$, $\theta > 1$ nonintegral.

We mention one result on continued fractions. Let $q_n(x)$ be the denominator of the nth approximating then

$$\lim_{n \to \infty} \int_0^1 (\log q_n(x) - \frac{1}{\log 2} \int_0^1 \frac{\log q_n(u)}{1+u}du)^2 \frac{1}{1+x}dx = 0.$$

He says that the *central limit theorem* and the *law of the iterated logarithm* for $\log q_n(x)$ also follow.

These results are strengthened in [Gordin 1971] such that $Tx = \theta x - \lfloor \theta x \rfloor$ and the map associated with the Jacobi-Perron algorithm are included.

Chapter 12

Lévy and the dual algorithm

Lévy's idea was to give a quite different proof for Gauss' conjecture. He starts with continued fractions in the following form [Lévy 1929].

$$X = a_0 + \frac{1}{x_1}, x_1 = a_1 + \frac{1}{x_2}, ..., x_n = a_n + \frac{1}{x_{n+1}}$$

where $a_n = \lfloor x_n \rfloor$, $x_0 = X$. Note that for $n \geq 1$ we have $x_n > 1$. Then he uses the relations

$$X = \frac{P_n x_n + P_{n-1}}{Q_n x_n + Q_{n-1}}$$

$$P_{n+1} = P_n a_n + P_{n-1}, Q_{n+1} = Q_n a_n + Q_{n-1}.$$

His interest lies in the probability law for x_n if X is chosen randomly. Therefore he then supposes $a_0 = 0$ and $0 < X < 1$. The probability of an interval dX is its length. Therefore the probability of $x_n \in]x, x + dx[$ is given as

$$f_n(x)dx = \sum \frac{dx}{(Q_n x + Q_{n-1})^2}, x > 1$$

where Q_n and Q_{n-1} are determined by $a_1, a_2, ..., a_{n-1}$. The probability that $x_n > x$ is

$$1 - F_n(x) = \int_x^\infty f_n(x)dx = \sum \frac{1}{Q_n(Q_n x + Q_{n-1})}.$$

Obviously the function $F(x)$ is defined by this relation and $F(0) = 1$ since

$$\sum \frac{1}{Q_n(Q_n + Q_{n-1})} = 1.$$

85

A translation into the language of measure theory would read

$$\lambda(x_n \in]x, x + dx[) = \int_x^{x+dx} \frac{dt}{(Q_n t + Q_{n-1})^2}.$$

He remarks that

$$f_1(x) = \frac{1}{x^2}, \; f_2(x) = \frac{1}{x^2} \sum_{a=1}^{\infty} f_1(a + \frac{1}{x})$$

and generally

$$f_{n+1} = \frac{1}{x^2} \sum_{a=1}^{\infty} f_n(a + \frac{1}{x}).$$

Furthermore the relation

$$1 - F_{n+1}(x) = \sum_{a=1}^{\infty} (F_n(a + \frac{1}{x}) - F_n(a))$$

holds.

Next he introduces $y_n = \frac{Q_{n+1}}{Q_n}$ and states $y_n = a_n + \frac{1}{y_{n-1}}$. The values of y_n are just rational numbers. If $y > 1$ is a rational number then $\beta_n(y)$ denotes the probability that $y = y_n$. Then

$$\beta_{n-1}(y) = \sum_{a=1}^{\infty} \beta_n(a + \frac{1}{y}).$$

If n is fixed and odd then $G(y)$ is the sum of the probabilities of the possible values of $y_n < y$. If n is even one has to add the probability of y. Obviously Lévy means that this probability is 0 if y is not a value of y_n. Then Lévy finds

$$1 - G_{n-1}(y) = \sum_{a=1}^{\infty} (G_n(a + \frac{1}{y}) - G(a)).$$

From the relation

$$\sum \frac{1}{Q_n(Q_n + Q_{n-1})} = 1$$

he concludes

$$\beta(\frac{q}{q'}) = \int_1^{\infty} \frac{dx}{(qx + q')^2} = \frac{1}{q(q + q')}$$

which now gives a precise definition of $\beta(y)$ if $y = \frac{q}{q'}$. He then transforms the foregoing relations into Stieltjes integrals

$$1 - F_n(x) = \sum \beta\left(\frac{Q_n}{Q_{n-1}}\right)\frac{\frac{Q_n}{Q_{n-1}} + 1}{\frac{Q_n}{Q_{n-1}}x + 1} = \int_1^\infty \frac{y+1}{yx+1}dG_{n-1}(y)$$

$$G_n(p+\eta) - G_n(p) = \int_{\frac{1}{\eta}}^\infty \frac{y(y+1)}{(py+1)((p+1)y+1)}dG_{n-1}(y).$$

The idea of Lévy's paper is also outlined in the chapter on Japanese continued fractions. If the limits $F(x) = \lim_{n\to\infty} F_n(x)$ and $G(y) = \lim_{n\to\infty} G_n(y)$ both exist then assuming that $G(y)$ is absolutely continuous (Lévy writes «il est naturel de supposer la continuité absolue») one finds

$$F(x) = \frac{1}{\log 2}\log\frac{2x}{x+1} = G(x).$$

Since the numbers y_n exhaust all rational numbers $y > 1$ as $n \to \infty$ it is easy to see that $G(y)$ is at least continuous. We remark that

$$\beta_n(y) = \frac{y(y+1)}{(py+1)((p+1)y+1)}\beta_{n-1}(y) \leq 2^{-n}.$$

Lévy then gives a rigorous proof for the uniform convergence of $F_n(x)$ and $G_n(y)$ and shows

$$|F_n(x) - F(x)| \leq (0.7)^{n-1}.$$

A variation of Lévy's proof was given in [Denjoy 1936]. But the hidden idea behind is the use of the *dual algorithm* or the *natural extension* of continued fractions.

The idea of a dual algorithm seems to go back to the so-called backward algorithm in [Nakada & Ito & Tanaka 1977]. The fibred system (B, T) is called a *dual fibred system* (or a *backward algorithm*) with respect to (B, T) if the following condition holds: The block of digits $(k_1, k_2, \ldots, k_n)$ is admissible for T if and only if $(k_n, \ldots, k_2, k_1)$ is an admissible block of digits for T^*. As usual $V(k_1, ..., k_n)$ denotes the inverse branches of T having Jacobians $\omega(k_1, ..., k_n)$ with respect to a given measure λ. In an obvious notation we write $V^*(k_n, \ldots, k_1)$ for the inverse branches T^* and $\omega^*(k_n, \ldots, k_1)$ for the Jacobians with respect to a given measure λ^* on B^*.

A measurable function $K : B \times B^* \to \mathbb{R}$ is called a *kernel* if

(a) $K \geq 0$

(b) $K\big(x, V^*(k)y\big)\omega^*(k; y) = K\big(V(k)x, y\big)\omega(k; x)$
   for all $x \in TB(k)$, $y \in T^*B^*(k)$ and $k \in I$.

In almost all known cases one gets a dual algorithm in the following way. If T is a piecewise fractional linear map which means

$$V(k)x = \frac{\gamma_k + \delta_k x}{\alpha_k + \beta_k x} \text{ for all digits } k \in I$$

then

$$V(k)^*y = \frac{\beta_k + \delta_k y}{\alpha_k + \gamma_k x} \text{ for all digits } k \in I$$

and the function

$$K(x, y) = \frac{1}{(1 + xy)^2}$$

is an appropriate kernel. Then the following question remains. Do the maps $V(k)^*$ belong to a fibred system on a set B^* which is a union of intervals so that you can take $\lambda_* = \lambda$ (Lebesgue measure)?
We first consider the case that $B = [0, 1]$ all cylinders of the fibred system (B, T) are *full* (or *proper*), i. e. $TB(k) = B$ for all $k \in I$ and $B^* = \bigcup_k B^*(k)$ is an interval. Then it is easy to give an explicit from for the invariant density for T, namely the integral

$$h(x) = \int_{B^*} K(x, y)dy$$

defines a T-invariant density.
We verify Kuzmin's equation:

$$\sum_k h\big(V(k)x\big)\omega(k; x) = \sum_k \int_{B^*} K\big(V(k)x, y\big)\omega(k; x)dy$$

$$= \sum_k \int_{B^*} K\big(x, V^*(k)y\big)\omega^*(k; y)dy = \sum_k \int_{B^*(k)} K\big(x, y\big)dy$$

$$= \int_{B^*} K(x, y)dy = h(x).$$

(1) Regular continued fractions
In this case one can take $T = T^*$ and obtains

$$h(x) = \int_0^1 \frac{1}{(1 + xy)^2}dy = \frac{1}{1 + x}.$$

(2) f-expansions with $f(x) = \frac{Ax}{1-Bx}$

Assume $B \neq 0$ and let f be defined on $[0, N]$ with the condition $AN = 1 + BN$ or on $[0, \infty[$ with $A = B$. The associated fibred system has the inverse branches

$$V(k)x = \frac{Ak + Ax}{Bk + 1 + Bx}, \quad k =, 1, ..., N - 1 \text{ or } \geq 0.$$

Since the transposed matrix gives a good guess one finds

$$V(k)^*y = \frac{B + Ay}{Bk + 1 + Aky}, \quad k =, 1, ..., N - 1 \text{ or } \geq 0.$$

The matrix equation

$$\begin{pmatrix} Bk + 1 & Ak \\ B & A \end{pmatrix} \begin{pmatrix} \alpha & \beta \\ \beta & \delta \end{pmatrix} = \begin{pmatrix} \alpha & \beta \\ \beta & \delta \end{pmatrix} \begin{pmatrix} Bk + 1 & B \\ Ak & A \end{pmatrix}$$

has a solution which does not depend on k (more on this device can be found in [Schweiger 2008]). Therefore the given fibred system on $B = [0, 1]$ can be mapped onto the dual fibred system on $B^* = [\frac{AB-B^2}{AB+A+A^2}, \frac{B}{1-A}]$ via the map

$$\psi(t) = \frac{-AB + B^2 t}{A^2 - A - ABt}.$$

If ψ is not constant this is an invertible map. The invariant density then is given as

$$h(x) = \int_{B^*} \frac{dy}{(1 + xy)^2}.$$

In a similar way the case $f(x) = \frac{C+Dx}{A+x}$ (with $C + DN = A + DN$) on $[1, N]$ or $[1, \infty[$ (with $D = 0$) has a dual on $[\frac{D}{AD-C-D^2}, \frac{D-1}{AD+D-C-D^2}]$.

However, that all cylinders of a fibred system are proper is just the ideal case. Since the dual algorithm reads the sequence of admissible digits in reverse order the situation may be more complex. We illustrate this with continued fractions to the nearest integer. Here

$$B =]-\frac{1}{2},\frac{1}{2}[$$

$$Tx = \frac{1}{x} - k, \text{ if } x \in B(k) = [\frac{1}{k+1},\frac{1}{k}[\cap] - \frac{1}{2},\frac{1}{2}[, \quad k \geq 2$$

$$Tx = -\frac{1}{x} + k, \text{ if } x \in B(k) =] - \frac{1}{k}, -\frac{1}{k+1}[\cap] - \frac{1}{2},\frac{1}{2}[, \quad k \leq -2$$

$$B^* = [0,\beta], \quad \beta = \frac{-1+\sqrt{5}}{2}$$

$$T^*y = -\frac{1}{y} - k, \text{ if } y \in B^*(k) =] - \frac{1}{k}, -\frac{1}{k+1-\beta}], \quad k \leq -2$$

$$T^*y = \frac{1}{y} - k, \text{ if } y \in B^*(k) =]\frac{1}{k+\beta},\frac{1}{k}], \quad k \geq 2.$$

The conditions on the digits for (B,T) are: if $|k_i| = 2$, then $k_{i+1} \geq 2$. These conditions are reflected for (B^*,T^*): If $k_i \leq -2$, then $|k_{i+1}| \geq 3$. Hence we have to change the domain of integration as follows.

$$D(x) = B^* = [0,\beta] \quad \text{for} \quad x > 0$$

$$D(x) = \bigcup_{|k_{i+1}|\geq 3} B^*(k) = [0,1-\beta] \quad \text{for} \quad x < 0.$$

Again $K(x,y) = (1+xy)^{-2}$ is a suitable kernel. Integration gives

$$h(x) = \int_0^\beta \frac{dy}{(1+xy)^2} = \frac{\beta}{1+\beta x} \quad \text{for} \quad x > 0,$$

and

$$h(x) = \int_0^{1-\beta} \frac{dy}{(1+xy)^2} = \frac{1-\beta}{1+(1-\beta)x}.$$

Note that $\frac{1}{1+\beta} = \beta$ and $\frac{1}{2+\beta} = 1 - \beta$.
More examples in this direction can be seen in the chapter on Japanese continued fractions. The case of β-expansions can be also discussed with a different method called *jump transformation*.

The dual algorithm is connected with the *natural extension* of a fibred system. The idea of a natural extension can be best illustrated with the one-sided shift

$$\tau : \Omega \to \Omega$$

on the space $\Omega = I^{\mathbb{N}}$, the space of all sequences

$$\omega = (\omega_1, \omega_2, \omega_3, ...)$$

which is defined by

$$\tau(\omega_1, \omega_2, \omega_3, ...) = (\omega_2, \omega_3, \omega_4, ...).$$

The space $\overline{\Omega} = I^{\mathbb{Z}}$ of all two-sided sequences

$$\overline{\omega} = (..., \omega_1, \omega_0, \omega_1, \omega_2, \omega_3, ...)$$

also allows a shift

$$\overline{\tau} : \overline{\Omega} \to \overline{\Omega}$$

defined by

$$\overline{\tau}(..., \omega_1, \omega_0, \omega_1, \omega_2, \omega_3, ...) = (..., w_1, w_0, w_1, w_2, w_3, ...)$$

with $w_k = \omega_{k+1}$.

This looks a little bit puzzling because one has the impression that $\overline{\tau} \circ \overline{\omega}$ is the same sequence but note that a two-sided sequence is a map from $\mathbb{Z}$ to I with $\overline{\omega}(k) = \omega_k$ but $\overline{\tau} \circ \overline{\omega}(k) = \omega_{k+1}$, a different map. Note that the shift $\overline{\tau}$ is an invertible map.

The dynamical system $(\overline{\Omega}, \overline{\tau})$ is called a *Bernoulli shift*. The map $\psi : \overline{\Omega} \to \Omega$ defined as

$$\psi(..., \omega_1, \omega_0, \omega_1, \omega_2, \omega_3, ...) = (\omega_1, \omega_2, \omega_3, ...)$$

satisfies the commutative law

$$\tau \circ \psi = \psi \circ \overline{\tau}.$$

One says that the one-sided shift has been *lifted* to the two-sided shift.

The Bernoulli shift represents something like the abstract idea of a natural extension. For f-expansions (or fibred systems) a realization as a map on a suitable subset of $\mathbb{R}^d$ is more interesting. We give two examples. The map

$$\overline{T}(x, y) = (gx - a, \frac{a + y}{g}), \ a = \lfloor gx \rfloor$$

is a natural extension of the g-adic map $Tx = gx - a$ and the map

$$\overline{T}(x, y) = (\frac{1}{x} - k, \frac{1}{k + y}), \ k = \lfloor \frac{1}{x} \rfloor$$

is a natural extension of the continued fraction map. The inverse branches of the dual algorithm T^* can be used to write down a natural extension for continued fractions to the nearest integer on $]-\frac{1}{2},\frac{1}{2}[\times]0,\beta[$.

A different extension was used occasionally. For continued fractions the following map is presented in [Einsiedler & Ward 2011]. This device may be due to the paper [Arnoux & Nogueira 1993] or even older. Define

$$Y = \{(x,y) : 0 < x \leq 1, 0 \leq y \leq \frac{1}{1+x}\}$$

and define the map

$$\tau(x,y) = (\frac{1}{x} - \lfloor\frac{1}{x}\rfloor, x - x^2 y).$$

Then one sees that this map is bijective and preserves area. The intervals $]\frac{1}{k+1},\frac{1}{k}]$ are mapped onto the "strips" $\{(x,y) : 0 < x \leq 1, \frac{1}{x+1+k} < y \leq \frac{1}{x+k}\}$. In fact, if $\tau(x,\frac{1}{1+x}) = (x',y')$ and $x = \frac{1}{k+x'}$ then $y' = \frac{1}{1+k+x'}$.

Chapter 13

Beta-expansions

Within two years three papers appeared which were concerned with the invariant measure for the β-adic map $Tx = \beta x - \lfloor \beta x \rfloor$. The paper [Gel'fond 1959] starts with the following result on q-adic maps ($q \geq 2$ an integer) which is attributed to [Hardy & Littlewood 1914]. Let

$$\alpha = \sum_{k=1}^{n} \frac{\lambda_k}{q^k} + \frac{x_{n+1}}{q^n}, \; 0 \leq x_{n+1} < 1, \; 0 \leq \lambda_k < q, \; x_{n+1} = x_{n+1}(\alpha)$$

and let $\psi(x) = 1, \, 0 \leq x \leq 1$ and $\psi(x) = 0$ for $x < 0$ or $1 < x$ then for almost all α we find

$$\lim_{N \to \infty} \frac{1}{N} \sum_{n=1}^{N} \psi(1 - t + x_n(\alpha)) = t, \; 0 < t \leq 1.$$

Now if $\theta > 1$, θ non-integral, and

$$\alpha == \sum_{k=1}^{n} \frac{\lambda_k}{\theta^k} + \frac{x_{n+1}}{\theta^n}, \; 0 \leq x_{n+1} < 1, \; 0 \leq \lambda_k < \theta, \; x_{n+1} = x_{n+1}(\alpha)$$

then there exists a function $\sigma(t)$ such that for almost all α

$$\lim_{N \to \infty} \frac{1}{N} \sum_{n=1}^{N} \psi(1 - t + x_n(\alpha)) = \sigma(t), \; 0 < t \leq 1.$$

If the expansion of $\alpha = 1$ is defined as

$$1 = \sum_{k=1}^{n} \frac{\lambda_k}{\theta^k} + \frac{t_{n+1}}{\theta^n}, \; 1 = t_1$$

and

$$\tau = \sum_{k=1}^{\infty} \frac{t_k}{\theta^{k-1}}$$

then he defines

$$\sigma_0(t) = \frac{1}{\tau} \sum_{k=1}^{\infty} \frac{\psi(1 - t_k + t)}{\theta^{k-1}}$$

and finds

$$\sigma(t) = \int_0^t \sigma_0(x)dx = \frac{1}{\tau} \sum_{k=1}^{\infty} \frac{\min(t, t_k)}{\theta^{k-1}}.$$

Since $\psi(1 - t + x_n) = 1$ exactly if $0 \le x_n \le t$ the result says how often the iterates $x_{n+1} = T^n \alpha$ visit the interval $]0, t]$. Therefore $\sigma(t)$ is the distribution function and $\sigma_0(t)$ the density of the associated invariant measure. The constant τ is the normalizing constant. Since Gel'fond does not use methods from ergodic theory he develops a rather long direct proof of his theorem. An important step is to prove

$$\int_0^1 \left(\frac{1}{N} \sum_{n=1}^N \psi(1 - t + x_n(\alpha)) - \sigma(t)\right)^2 d\alpha = O\left(\frac{1}{N}\right).$$

At a certain point he uses that the set of rational numbers is countable which is similar to the proof of the *individual ergodic theorem*.

He also investigates the function $\sigma_0(t)$. This function has finitely many jumps if $t_k = t_{k+p}$ for some $k \ge 1$ and $p \ge 1$ which means that the expansion of $\alpha = 1$ eventually becomes periodic. A real algebraic number is called a *Pisot number* if $\theta > 1$ and all its conjugates $\theta_1, ..., \theta_\nu$ lie inside a circle $|z| \le \rho < 1$. It is shown that when $\theta > 1$ is a Pisot number then $\sigma_0(t)$ has only finitely many steps.

Cigler in his paper [Cigler 1960] refers to Gel'fond. He first shows by direct calculation that for any continuous function f the equality

$$\int_0^1 f(\theta t)\sigma_0(t)dt = \int_0^1 f(t)\sigma_0(t)dt.$$

Therefore $\sigma_0(t)$ is the density of an invariant measure. Then he shows that the map $Tx = \theta x - \lfloor \theta x \rfloor$ is ergodic which ensures the uniqueness of the invariant measure (up to a multiplicative constant) which is absolutely continuous with respect to Lebesgue measure. He applies *Lebesgue's density theorem* (see e. g.

[Natanson 1955&1961] to the cylinders which he calls *Grundintervalle*. These are the intervals

$$J = \{x : \lambda_1(x) = \lambda_1, ..., \lambda_n(x) = \lambda_n\} = [\frac{\lambda_1}{\theta} + ... + \frac{\lambda_n}{\theta^n}, \frac{\lambda_1}{\theta} + ... + \frac{\lambda_n^*}{\theta^n}[$$

where $\lambda_n^* \leq \lambda_n + 1$. Let $T^{-1}E = E$ and denote by $c_E(x)$ its indicator function. Then

$$\lambda(E \cap J) = \int_{\frac{\lambda_1}{\theta}+...+\frac{\lambda_n}{\theta^n}}^{\frac{\lambda_1}{\theta}+...+\frac{\lambda_n^*}{\theta^n}} c_E(x)dx = \int_{\frac{\lambda_1}{\theta}+...+\frac{\lambda_n}{\theta^n}}^{\frac{\lambda_1}{\theta}+...+\frac{\lambda_n^*}{\theta^n}} c_E(\theta x)dx$$

$$= \frac{1}{\theta}\int_{\frac{\lambda_2}{\theta}+...+\frac{\lambda_n}{\theta^{n-1}}}^{\frac{\lambda_2}{\theta}+...+\frac{\lambda_n^*}{\theta^{n-1}}} c_E(x)dx = \frac{1}{\theta^n}\int_0^{\lambda_n^*-\lambda_n} c_E(x)dx.$$

However, Cigler does not explain how to come to the final estimate

$$\lambda(E \cap J) \leq \lambda(E)\lambda(J).$$

The gap in the proof can be closed if one restricts to the subclass of *proper cylinders* for which $\lambda_n^* - \lambda_n = 1$. Since every cylinder is the union of proper cylinders modulo a set of measure 0 this can be done.
In a final theorem Cigler shows that the blocks $(\lambda_{\nu+1}, ..., \lambda_{\nu+n})$ form a *Markov chain* if the expansion of 1 is finite, i. e.

$$1 = \frac{a_1}{\theta} + ... + \frac{a_{n+1}}{\theta^{n+1}}.$$

The most complete account on β-expansions is [Parry 1960]. Following Rényi he uses the notation

$$x = \varepsilon_0(x) + \frac{\varepsilon_1(x)}{\beta} + \frac{\varepsilon_2(x)}{\beta^2} + ...$$

First Kuzmin's equation for $Tx = \beta x - \lfloor \beta x \rfloor$ is presented as

$$\beta h(x) = \sum_{Ty=x} h(y) = \sum_{m=0}^{\lfloor \beta x \rfloor} h(\frac{x+m}{\beta}).$$

Then the form

$$h(x) = \sum_{x < T^n 1} \frac{1}{\beta^n}$$

is proven. The density $h(x)$ has finitely many steps if β has a recurrent tail. Such numbers are called β-*numbers*. If $\varepsilon_0(\beta) = 0$ for $n \geq n_0$ then β is called a *simple* β-*number*. Then he discusses the question when a series

$$x = b_0(x) + \frac{b_1(x)}{\beta} + \frac{b_2(x)}{\beta^2} + \dots.$$

is the β-expansion of x. He shows that but one exception the β-expansion of

$$1 = a_0(x) + \frac{a_1(x)}{\beta} + \frac{a_2(x)}{\beta^2} + \dots.$$

gives a criterion. It is necessary and sufficient that for all $n \geq 0$ the condition

$$(b_n, b_{n+1}, b_{n+2}, \dots) \prec (a_0, a_1, a_2, \dots)$$

holds. The sign $\prec$ denotes lexicographic order. A typical exception is as follows. Let $\beta^2 = 2\beta + 1$ then

$$\eta = 2 + \frac{1}{\beta} \equiv (2, 1, 0, 0, \dots)$$

but also

$$\beta = 2 + \frac{2}{\beta^2} + \frac{2}{\beta^4} + \dots \equiv (2, 0, 2, 0, \dots).$$

An interesting result is the theorem that the conjugates of a β-number have absolute value less than 2. The set of simple β-numbers is dense in $[0, \infty[$. At the end Parry uses Birkhoff's *Ergodic Theorem*. If μ is the normalized invariant measure the frequency of digits is calculated.
The normalizing factor

$$F(\beta) = \int_0^1 h(x)dx$$

is considered. It is easy to prove the inequality

$$1 \leq F(\beta) \leq \frac{\beta}{\beta - 1}.$$

If β is a simple β-number then

$$\lim_{\gamma \to \beta - 0} F(\gamma) = F(\beta) \frac{\beta^n}{\beta^n - 1}.$$

If β is not a simple β-number then

$$\lim_{\gamma \to \beta - 0} F(\gamma) = F(\beta).$$

Generally the equation

$$\lim_{\gamma \to \beta+0} F(\gamma) = F(\beta)$$

holds. Last but not least

$$\lim_{\gamma \to 1+0} F(\gamma) = \infty.$$

To verify the last result it is sufficient to consider the numbers $\beta(n) > 1$ which are solutions of the equation $x^{n+1} - x^n - 1 = 0$. Then

$$F(\beta(n)) = \frac{1}{\beta(n)} + (n+1)(\beta(n) - 1).$$

Parry proves that if $K > 1$ is an arbitrary constant then for sufficiently great values of n we have $\beta(n) - 1 \geq \frac{K}{n}$.

An easy way to determine the invariant measure for β-expansions is the use of *jump transformations* (see [Schweiger 1995]). Denote by $\mathcal{Z}$ the set of all cylinders of a fibred system (B, T). Let $\mathcal{A} \subseteq \mathcal{Z}$ be a fixed subclass. Then put

$$\mathcal{B}_n = \{B(k_1, ..., k_n) : B(k_1, ..., k_s) \notin \mathcal{A}, 1 \leq s \leq n-1, B(k_1, ..., k_n) \in \mathcal{A}\}$$

$$\mathcal{D}_n = \{B(k_1, ..., k_n) : B(k_1, ..., k_n) \notin \mathcal{A}, 1 \leq s \leq n\}$$

$$B_n = \bigcup_{E \in \mathcal{B}_n} E, \ D_0 = B, \ D_n = \bigcup_{E \in \mathcal{D}_n} E, \ W = \bigcap_{s=0}^{\infty} D_s.$$

The map

$$S : B \to B, \ Sx = T^n x \quad \text{if} \quad x \in B_n$$

is called the jump transformation (with respect to $\mathcal{A}$).

The jump transformation can help to find an invariant measure for T. The reason is the following lemma.

Let ν be an invariant measure with respect to S. Then

$$\mu(E) := \sum_{n=0}^{\infty} \nu(T^{-n} E \cap D_n)$$

defines a measure which is invariant with respect to T.

The proof is easy. Note that $S^{-1}E = \bigcup_{n=1}^{\infty}(B_n \cap T^{-n}E)$. Then

$$
\begin{aligned}
\mu(T^{-1}E) &= \sum_{n=0}^{\infty} \nu(T^{-n-1}E \cap D_n) \\
&= \sum_{n=0}^{\infty} \nu(T^{-n-1}E \cap B_{n+1}) + \sum_{n=0}^{\infty} \nu(T^{-n-1}E \cap D_{n+1}) \\
&= \nu\left(S^{-1}E\right) + \sum_{n=1}^{\infty} \nu(T^{-n}E \cap D_n) \\
&= \nu(E) + \sum_{n=1}^{\infty} \nu(T^{-n}E \cap D_n) = \mu(E).
\end{aligned}
$$

Note that if ν is a finite measure and $\sum_{n=1}^{\infty} \nu(D_n) < \infty$, then μ is finite too.

Now let $Tx = \beta x - \lfloor \beta x \rfloor$ be the β-adic map. We take $\mathcal{A}$ as the class of all full cylinders. Then clearly Lebesgue measure λ is invariant for S. Since $\lambda(D_n) \leq \beta^{-n}$, the measure

$$
\mu(E) = \sum_{n=0}^{\infty} \lambda(T^{-n}E \cap D_n)
$$

is a finite invariant measure. Now we observe that $T^n D_n = [0, T^n 1[$. Then the density of μ is given by

$$
h(x) = \sum_{x < T^n 1} \beta^{-n}.
$$

The set $\{0, 1, ..., s\}$ can be seen as a discrete topological space. Then the set $S = \{0, 1, ..., s\}^{\mathbb{N}_0}$ is a topological space by the *product topology*. In this space the *shift operator* defined as

$$
\sigma(x_0, x_1, x_2, ...) = (x_1, x_2, x_3, ...)
$$

is a continuous map. A compact subset $X \subseteq S$ which is invariant under σ, i. e. , $\sigma X = X$ is called a *symbolic dynamic system*. Furthermore, two piecewise continuous maps $S : [0, 1[\to [0, 1[$ and $T : [0, 1[\to [0, 1[$ are said to be *conjugate* if there exists a homeomorphism $\phi : [0, 1[\to [0, 1[$ such that

$$
\phi \circ S = T \circ \phi.
$$

A corollary of the investigations of symbolic dynamic systems in [Parry 1966] is the following. Let

$$
Tx = f^{-1}x - \lfloor f^{-1}x \rfloor
$$

be an f-expansion defined by a strictly increasing differentiable function $f :$
$[0, \tau[\to [0, 1[, \tau > 1$ such that $0 < f'(x) < 1$ and

$$Sx = \beta x - \lfloor \beta x \rfloor, \, \beta > 1$$

a β-adic map then T and S are conjugate. The number β is given by the fact
that conjugate maps have the same *entropy*, therefore

$$\log \beta = h(S) = h(T) = \int_0^1 \log |T'x| d\nu(x)$$

where ν denotes the absolutely continuous invariant measure for T.

Chapter 14

Japanese continued fractions

T. E. McKinney introduced λ-continued fractions [McKinney 1907]. The underlying map is given as $f_\lambda : [\lambda - 1, \lambda] \to [\lambda - 1, \lambda]$ defined as

$$f_\lambda(x) = \frac{\varepsilon}{x} - \lfloor \frac{\varepsilon}{x} + 1 - \lambda \rfloor$$

for $x \neq 0$ and $\varepsilon = \text{sign } x$. Though this paper is mentioned shortly in [Perron 1954:174] it seems that this paper went unnoticed.

However, a systematic study of continued fractions of this type was undertaken by several writers from Japan. The starting point of [Nakada, Ito & Tanaka 1977] is a kind of guided guess for the invariant measure for (regular) continued fractions. Behind Lévy's idea there is hidden the dual algorithm (see also the discussion of the paper [Lévy 1929]). Put

$$f_n(x) = \sum_{a_1, a_2, \ldots, a_n} \frac{1}{(q_n + q_{n-1}x)^2}.$$

A discrete probability measure G_n is introduced. To every point

$$\frac{q_{n-1}}{q_n} = \cfrac{1}{a_n + \cfrac{1}{a_{n-1} + \ldots + \cfrac{1}{a_1}}}$$

the mass $\frac{1}{q_n(q_n + q_{n-1})}$ is assigned. Then

$$f_n(x) = \sum_{a_1, a_2, \ldots, a_n} \frac{1 + \frac{q_{n-1}}{q_n}}{(1 + \frac{q_{n-1}}{q_n}x)^2} G_n(\{\frac{q_{n-1}}{q_n}\}) = \int_0^1 \frac{1 + y}{(1 + xy)^2} dG_n(y).$$

If $p \geq 1$ is an integer then

$$\int_{\frac{1}{p+x}}^{\frac{1}{p}} dG_n(y) = \sum_{\frac{1}{p+x} \leq \frac{q_{n-1}}{q_n} \leq \frac{1}{p}} \frac{1}{q_n(q_n + q_{n-1})}$$

$$= \sum_{a_n = p, \, 0 \leq \frac{q_{n-2}}{q_{n-1}} \leq x} \frac{1}{(pq_{n-1} + q_{n-2})((p+1)q_{n-1} + q_{n-2})}$$

$$= \int_0^x \frac{1+y}{(p+y)(p+1+y)} dG_{n-1}(y).$$

If one assumes that the sequence (G_n) converges weakly to a probability measure G which has a continuous density $g(y)$ then we obtain by differentiating

$$\frac{1}{(p+x)^2} g\left(\frac{1}{p+x}\right) = \frac{1+x}{(p+x)(p+1+x)} g(x)$$

or

$$\left(1 + \frac{1}{p+x}\right) g\left(\frac{1}{p+x}\right) = (1+x)g(x) = h(x).$$

Therefore $h(x) = C$. From the viewpoint of ergodic theory this is clear since $h(x)$ is invariant against the transformation $Tx = \frac{1}{x} - p$.

The core of the paper is to apply this method to the real part of Hurwitz' generalization of continued fractions [Hurwitz 1888]. This is the map S on the set $[-\frac{1}{2}, \frac{1}{2}] \setminus \{0\}$ defined by

$$Sx = \frac{1}{x} - \lfloor \frac{1}{x} + \frac{1}{2} \rfloor.$$

The digits are defined as

$$a_1(x) = \lfloor \frac{1}{x} + \frac{1}{2} \rfloor, \quad a_n(x) = a_1(S^{n-1}x).$$

A finite sequence $(a_1, a_2, a_3, ...)$ is called *S-admissible* if $|a_i| \geq 2$ for $1 \leq i \leq n$ and if $a_i = 2$ then $a_{i+1} \geq 2$ while if $a_i = -2$ then $a_{i+1} \leq -2$. If

$$\psi(a_1, ..., a_n)x = \cfrac{1}{a_1 + ... + \cfrac{1}{a_n + x}}$$

then $\psi(a_1, ..., a_n)$ is defined on $] -\frac{1}{2}, \frac{1}{2}[$ if $|a_n| \geq 3$, $]0, \frac{1}{2}[$ if $a_n = 2$ and $] -\frac{1}{2}, 0[$ if $a_n = -2$.

Quantities p_n and q_n are defined in a similar way as for regular continued fractions. Note that

$$\frac{q_{n-1}}{q_n} = \cfrac{1}{a_n + \cfrac{1}{q_{n-1} + ... + \cfrac{1}{a_1}}}.$$

However if $(a_1, ..., a_n)$ is an S-admissible block the reverse block $(a_1, ..., a_1)$ may not be S-admissible. The following lemma which can be found in [Perron 1954] is the key to find a *backward transformation*. If $(a_1, ..., a_n)$ is S-admissible then

$$\alpha = \sup_{(a_1,...,a_n)} \frac{q_{n-1}}{q_n} = \frac{\sqrt{5}-1}{2}, \quad \beta = \sup_{(a_1,...,a_n),a_n \neq 2} = \frac{3-\sqrt{5}}{2}.$$

Fortunately there are no gaps between α and β which means it is possible to define a new map S^* by

$$S^* x = \frac{1}{x} - \lfloor \frac{1}{x} + \alpha \rfloor, \, x > 0$$

$$S^* 0 = 0$$

$$S^* x = \frac{1}{x} + \lfloor -\frac{1}{x} + \beta \rfloor, \, x < 0.$$

Digits are defined as

$$a_1^*(x) = \lfloor \frac{1}{x} + \alpha \rfloor, \, x > 0, \, a_1^*(x) = -\lfloor -\frac{1}{x} + \alpha \rfloor, \, x < 0$$

$$a_n^*(x) = a_1^*((S^*)^{n-1} x).$$

Then every $x \in [-\alpha, \alpha]$ has an expansion

$$x = \cfrac{1}{a_1^* + \cfrac{1}{a_2^* + ... + \cfrac{1}{a_n^* + (S^*)^n x}}}.$$

The point is that a sequence $(a_1, a_2, ..., a_n)$ is S^*-admissible if and only if $(a_n, a_{n-1}, .., a_1)$ is S-admissible. This means: If $a_i^* \geq 2$ then $a_{i+1}^* \neq -2$ an if $a_i^* \leq -2$ then $a_{i+1}^* \neq 2$. Since S is ergodic and admits an invariant measure it is further shown that S^* is ergodic and admits an invariant measure too. Here

symbolic spaces and *natural extensions* are used.
The path of Lévy is followed. If

$$\frac{q_{n-1}}{q_n} = \cfrac{1}{a_n + \cfrac{1}{a_{n-1} + \ldots + \cfrac{1}{a_1}}}$$

then a mass is assigned as follows.

$$G_n\{\frac{q_{n-1}}{q_n}\} = \frac{1}{(q_n + \frac{1}{2}q_{n-1})(q_n - \frac{1}{2}q_{n-1})}, \quad |a_n| \geq 3$$

$$G_n\{\frac{q_{n-1}}{q_n}\} = \frac{1}{2(q_n + \frac{1}{2}q_{n-1})q_n}, \quad a_n = 2$$

$$G_n\{\frac{q_{n-1}}{q_n}\} = \frac{1}{2(q_n - \frac{1}{2}q_{n-1})q_n}, \quad a_n = -2.$$

Then one has to distinguish the cases (i) $-\beta < a < x < \beta$, (ii) $\beta < a < x < \alpha$, and (iii) $-\alpha < a < x - \beta$ and finds seven different equations. We mention just one case, namely

$$(1 - \frac{1}{4}(p + x)^2)g(\frac{1}{p + x}) = (1 - \frac{1}{4}x^2)g(x), \quad -\beta < x < \beta, \ |p| \geq 3.$$

Then again the function

$$h(x) = 2(1 - \frac{1}{2}x)g(x), \quad -\alpha < x < \beta$$

$$h(x) = (1 - \frac{1}{4}x^2)g(x), \quad -\beta < x < \beta$$

$$h(x) = 2(1 + \frac{1}{2}x)g(x), \quad \beta < x < \alpha$$

satisfies the equation $h(x) = h(S^*x)$. Since S^* is ergodic h must be constant almost everywhere.
Therefore the invariant measure can be written down explicitly.
In a similar way one finds the invariant density for S, namely

$$\frac{d\mu}{d\lambda}(x) = \frac{1}{(1 + x\alpha)(1 - x\beta)}, \quad x > 0$$

$$\frac{d\mu}{d\lambda}(x) = \frac{1}{(1 - x\alpha)(1 + x\beta)}, \ x > 0.$$

It is interesting that the *kernel* $K(x, y) = \frac{1}{(1+xy)^2}$ is not used. This would give
the representation

$$\frac{d\mu}{d\lambda}(x) = \int_{-\beta}^{\alpha} \frac{dy}{(1 + xy)^2}, \ x > 0$$

$$\frac{d\mu}{d\lambda}(x) = \int_{-\alpha}^{\beta} \frac{dy}{(1 + xy)^2}, \ x < 0.$$

For $0 \le \alpha \le 1$ in [Nakada 1981] λ-fractions were rediscovered. He treats the
map

$$Tx = \left| \frac{1}{x} \right| - \lfloor \left| \frac{1}{x} \right| + 1 - \alpha \rfloor.$$

The related map

$$Tx = \frac{1}{x} - \lfloor \frac{1}{x} + 1 - \alpha \rfloor$$

was considered in [Tanaka & Ito 1981].

Chapter 15

Discontinuous Groups

Another extension of continued fractions goes back to [Rosen 1954]. Rosen studies the coefficients of the linear fractional transformations

$$V(z) = \frac{az+b}{cz+d}, \ ad - bc = 1$$

in the group $\Gamma(\lambda)$ generated by the maps

$$S(z) = z + \lambda, \ T(z) = -\frac{1}{z}.$$

According to [Hecke 1936] this group is discontinuous (a *Fuchsian group*) if $\lambda = 2 \cos \frac{\pi}{q}$, $q \geq 3$ when $\lambda < 2$ and also for every real $\lambda > 2$. If $U(z) = S(T(z))$ then for $\lambda = 2 \cos \frac{\pi}{q}$, $q \geq 3$ we find $U^q(z) = z$. Note that $2 \cos \frac{\pi}{3} = 1$, $2 \cos \frac{\pi}{4} = \sqrt{2}$, $2 \cos \frac{\pi}{5} = \frac{1+\sqrt{5}}{2}$, and $2 \cos \frac{\pi}{6} = \sqrt{3}$.

We first recall the definition of a *fundamental region* D of a group Γ which operates on a subset $E \subseteq \mathbb{C}$. For any $z \in E$ there is a $w \in E$ and a group element $\gamma \in \Gamma$ such that $z = \gamma(w)$ and D is minimal with this property. As an example we take the group

$$\Gamma = \{a_1 \omega_1 + a_2 \omega_2 : a_1, a_2 \in \mathbb{Z}, \ \frac{\omega_1}{\omega_2} \text{ is not real}\}$$

and $E = \mathbb{C}$. Then the parallelogram

$$D = \{t_1 \omega_1 + t_2 \omega_2 : 0 \leq t_1 < 1, \ 0 \leq t_2 < 1\}$$

107

is a fundamental region for Γ.

Rosen is interested in the expression of a member of the group $\Gamma(\lambda)$ as a *word* in T and S, namely

$$V = S^{r_0} T S^{r_1} T \cdots T S^{r_n}$$

with integers r_j, $0 \leq j \leq n$. The group $\Gamma(\lambda)$ possesses a standard fundamental region defined by

$$-\frac{\lambda}{2} \leq \mathfrak{Re} z \leq \frac{\lambda}{2}, \, 1 \leq |z|.$$

If $0 < \lambda < 2$ then the set of *limit points* is a perfect everywhere dense subset of $\mathbb{R}$. If $2 < \lambda$ this set is a perfect nowhere dense subset of $\mathbb{R}$.

Due to the relation $(TS)^q = \mathbf{1}$ for $0 < \lambda < 2$ different words may define the same substitution. It is proved that two words define the same substitution if and only if a certain standard form (called *reduced form*) are identical. Then the word V corresponds to a finite λ-*fraction*

$$r_o + \cfrac{\varepsilon_1}{r_1 \lambda + \cfrac{\varepsilon_2}{r_2 \lambda + \ldots}}, \, r_0 \geq 0, r_j \geq 1, |\varepsilon_j| = 1, j \geq 1.$$

The substitution

$$V(z) = \frac{Az + B}{Cz + D}$$

belongs to $\Gamma(\lambda)$ if

$$\frac{A}{C} = V(\infty) = r_o + \cfrac{\varepsilon_1}{r_1 \lambda + \cfrac{\varepsilon_2}{r_2 \lambda + \ldots}}.$$

The following algorithm is given for $0 < \lambda < 2$. If α is a real number then the following sequence if formed

$$\alpha = r_0 \lambda + \varepsilon_1 a_1, \, r_0 = \lfloor \frac{\alpha}{\lambda} + \frac{1}{2} \rfloor, \, 0 \leq a_1 \leq \frac{\lambda}{2}$$

$$1 = a_1 r_1 \lambda + \varepsilon_2 a_2, \, r_1 = \lfloor \frac{1}{a_1 \lambda} + \frac{1}{2} \rfloor, \, 0 \leq a_2 \leq \frac{\lambda a_1}{2}$$

$$a_1 = a_2 r_2 \lambda + \varepsilon_3 a_3, \, r_2 = \lfloor \frac{a_1}{a_2 \lambda} + \frac{1}{2} \rfloor, \, 0 \leq a_3 \leq \frac{\lambda a_2}{2}$$

$$\ldots$$

$$a_i = a_{i+1} r_{i+1} \lambda + \varepsilon_{i+1} a_{i+2}, \, r_{i+1} = \lfloor \frac{a_{i+1}}{\lambda a_{i+2}} + \frac{1}{2} \rfloor, \, 0 \leq a_{i+2} \leq \frac{\lambda a_{i+1}}{2}.$$

This gives the expansion

$$\alpha = r_o + \cfrac{\varepsilon_1}{r_1\lambda + \cfrac{\varepsilon_2}{r_2\lambda + ...}}$$

which may terminate or not but it gives a reduced λ-fraction for $\lambda = 2\cos\frac{\pi}{q}$, $q \geq 4$. For $2 < \lambda$ the formal process starts as before but not every real number can be expanded. Take $\lambda = \sqrt{5}$ then

$$\frac{29}{4\sqrt{5}} = 1 \cdot \sqrt{5} + \frac{9}{4\sqrt{5}}, \ \frac{4\sqrt{5}}{9} = 0 \cdot \sqrt{5} + \frac{4\sqrt{5}}{9}.$$

Therefore $r_i = 0$ for all $i \geq 1$. This corresponds to the fact that the set of limit points is a nowhere dense subset.

Later the metrical properties of Rosen's λ-fractions were considered (see e. g. the paper [Burton & Kraaikamp & Schmidt 2000]). Note that these continued fractions are different from McKinney's expansions (see the chapter Japanese Continued Fractions). One uses the map

$$T : [-\frac{\lambda}{2}, \frac{\lambda}{2}[\mapsto [-\frac{\lambda}{2}, \frac{\lambda}{2}[$$

$$\varepsilon_1(x) = \text{sgn}x, \ r_1(x) = \lfloor \frac{\varepsilon_1}{x\lambda} + \frac{1}{2} \rfloor$$

$$Tx = \frac{\varepsilon_1}{x} - r_1(x).$$

By the way, this map explains what happens with $\lambda = \sqrt{5}$. All points x with $\frac{2}{\sqrt{5}} < x < \frac{\sqrt{5}}{2}$ have $r_1(x) = 0$ and $T^2x = x$.

A generalization was made in [Dajani & Kraaikamp & Steiner 2009]. Let α be an additional parameter, $\frac{1}{2} \leq \alpha \leq \frac{1}{\lambda}$, and consider the fibred system on the interval $[\lambda(\alpha - 1), \lambda\alpha]$

$$Tx = |\frac{1}{x}| - \lambda d(x), \ d(x) = \lfloor |\frac{1}{x\lambda}| + 1 - \alpha \rfloor.$$

The main interest in this research is the construction of the *natural extension* as a planar map with application to Diophantine approximations.

There are many interesting links between continued fractions and geodesics. We mention just one out of many papers [Series 1985] (see also [Series 2003] for connections between hyperbolic geometry and dynamics).

Chapter 16

Ergodic Maps

The backbone of most of today's metrical theory is ergodic theory (for its history we refer to [von Plato 1994]; the historical development of the closely related theory of integration can be found in [Hawkins 1975]). Ergodic theory was not just applied to maps like $Tx = 2x - \lfloor 2x \rfloor$ or $Tx = \frac{1}{x} - \lfloor \frac{1}{x} \rfloor$ but was also developed by issues around these maps. Here we sketch some notions of ergodic theory. For more information we refer to the ample literature (e, g. [Arnold & Avez 1967], [Billingsley 1965], [Dajani & Kraaikamp 2002], [Hopf 1937], [Jacobs 1960], [Kac 1959], [Sinai 1994]).

As a first attempt the following classical result which is attributed to [Kronecker 1884] (see also [Jacobi 1835]). Let x be an irrational number and form the sequence $x - n_1, 2x - n_2, 3x - n_3, ...$ where $x_j = jx - n_j \in [0, 1[$, then these numbers are *dense* in the unit interval $[0, 1[$. Since x is an irrational number the points $x_j = jx - n_j$ are all distinct. Therefore for any given $\varepsilon > 0$ there are numbers $n \neq m$ such $0 < x_n - x_m < \varepsilon$. Given a subinterval $[a, b[$ and $0 < 2\varepsilon < b - a$ then there is an integer p such that $a < p(x_n - x_m) < b$ and so $p(n - m)x - p(n_j - m_j) \in [a, b[$. This says that there are integers A, B such that $Ax - B \in [a, b[$ which just means that the sequence mentioned before is dense.

The beginning of *uniform distribution* was then the following result. Let

$$A([a, b[; N, x) = \#\{0 \leq n < N : x_n \in [a, b[\}$$

then

$$\lim_{N \to \infty} \frac{A([a, b[; N, x)}{N} = \lambda([a, b[) = b - a.$$

The starting point was [Weyl 1916]. Further information can be found in [Hlawka 1984] and in [Kuipers & Niederreiter 1974], say.

Let X be a space equipped with a σ-algebra ($= \sigma$-field) of sets $\mathcal{F}$ and $T : X \to X$ be a measurable map. This means that $A \in \mathcal{F}$ implies $T^{-1}A \in \mathcal{F}$. The sets $E \in \mathcal{F}$ are called measurable. Furthermore a finite or σ-finite measure P is given on $\mathcal{F}$. The measure P is called finite if $P(X) < \infty$. It is called σ-finite if X is the countable union of subsets with finite measure.

The map is called non-singular if $P(A) = 0$ implies $P(T^{-1}A) = 0$. It is usual to consider only non-singular maps in ergodic theory. One says that T preserves the measure P or P is an invariant measure if $P(A) = P(T^{-1}A)$ for all $A \in \mathcal{F}$. Let us consider some examples.

(1) Let I be a finite or countable set and put $X = I^{\mathbb{N}}$, the set of all sequences $\omega = (i_1, i_2, i_3, ...)$, $i_k = i_k(\omega) \in I$. A cylinder is a set of the form

$$Z = \{\omega : (i_n(\omega), i_{n+1}(\omega), ..., i_{n+k-1}(\omega)) = (a_1, a_2, ..., a_k)\}.$$

Then $\mathcal{F}$ is the σ-algebra generated by the cylinders. There is a natural map, the shift τ defined by

$$\tau(i_1, i_2, i_3, ...) = (i_2, i_3, i_4, ...).$$

The connection to f-expansions is immediate. If $Tx = 2x - \lfloor 2x \rfloor$, say, then take $I = \{0, 1\}$ and the map $\Phi : [0, 1[\to I^{\mathbb{N}}$ defined by

$$\Phi(\sum_{k=1}^{\infty} \frac{a_k}{2^k}) = (a_1, a_2, a_3, ...).$$

Then the relation $\Phi(Tx) = \tau(\Phi x)$ holds. The same is true for the continued fraction map $Tx = \frac{1}{x} - \lfloor \frac{1}{x} \rfloor$ with $I = \mathbb{N}$. On the shift space $X = I^{\mathbb{N}}$ many measures can be defined. The easiest examples are given by fixing probabilities $p(i)$, $i \in I$, $0 \le p(i) \le 1$, $\sum_{i \in I} p(i) = 1$ and defining

$$P(Z) = p(a_1)...p(a_k).$$

It is not obvious that this definition leads to a measure on the σ-algebra $\mathcal{F}$. One can use the general theory of product measures. Clearly the measure P is invariant. The most common example is $I = \{0, 1\}$. The choice $p(0) = p(1) = \frac{1}{2}$ corresponds to Lebesgue measure on $[0, 1[$ in the following sense, namely

$$P(\Phi^{-1}E) = \lambda(E)$$

for a measurable set $A \subseteq [0, 1[$.

(2) Very often invariant subspaces $Y \subseteq X = I^{\mathbb{N}}$ are of interest. A subset

Y is called invariant if $\tau Y \subseteq Y$. Examples are given by β-expansions $Tx = \beta x - \lfloor \beta x \rfloor$, $\beta > 1$ and non-integral. Let us take $\beta = \frac{1+\sqrt{5}}{2}$ then

$$TB(0) = T[0, \frac{1}{\beta}[= [0, 1[$$

and

$$TB(1) = T[\frac{1}{\beta}, 1[= [0, \frac{1}{\beta}[.$$

This means that the block of digits 01 is not admitted. The corresponding subspace Y is given by all sequences $\omega = (i_1, i_2, i_3, ...)$, $i_k \in \{0, 1\}$, with the property that if $i_k = 1$ then $i_{k+1} = 0$. This leads to the question which invariant subspaces correspond to f-expansions and to *sofic systems* (see e. g. [Krieger 1987, 1984], [Fischer 1975], [Weiss 1973]).
(3) One can also consider the space $\Omega = I^{\mathbb{Z}}$ of all two-sided sequences. The shift is defined in a similar way. If $\omega = (..., i_{-2}, i_{-1}, i_0, i_1, i_2, i_3, ...)$ then $\tau \omega = (..., j_{-2}, j_{-1}, j_0, j_1, j_2, j_3, ...)$ where $j_k = i_{k+1}$. Cylinders are defined in an obvious way. If we define $P\{\omega : i_n(\omega) = k\} = p_k$ and the random variables $i_n(\omega)$ are independent this system is called a *Bernoulli shift*.
(4) Let take $X = \mathbb{R} \setminus A$ with the usual Lebesgue measure λ. Then take

$$Tx = x - \frac{1}{x} \qquad .$$

the so-called *Boole's transformation*. The definition explains the removal of the set $A = \{x : T^n x = 0 \text{ for some } n \geq 0\}$. It is easy to see that λ is invariant. If $E =]\eta, \xi[$ then $T^{-1}E =]\eta_1, \xi_1[\cup]\eta_2, \xi_2[$. The numbers ξ_1 and ξ_2 are the roots of $x^2 - \xi x - 1 = 0$, hence $\xi_1 + \xi_2 = \xi$. In a similar way $\eta_1 + \eta_2 = \eta$. Then

$$\lambda(E) = \xi - \eta = \xi_1 + \xi_2 - (\eta_1 + \eta_2) = \xi_1 - \eta_1 + \xi_2 - \eta_2 = \lambda(T^{-1}E).$$

A set is called *invariant* if $T^{-1}E = E$. The map T is called *ergodic* if for an invariant set E the condition $P(E) = 0$ or $P(X \setminus E) = 0$ holds. In the early days of ergodic theory the names *indecomposable* and *metrically transitive* were used. The condition $T^{-1}E = E$ can be replaced by the slightly more general condition $P((T^{-1}E \setminus E) \cup (E \setminus T^{-1}E)) = 0$. A map is called *conservative* if there are no *wandering sets* with positive measure, i. e. if W is a set such all preimages $T^{-1}W, T^{-2}W, T^{-3}W, ...$ are pairwise disjoint then $P(W) = 0$. If the measure P is invariant and finite then there are no wandering sets with positive measure. This is called the *recurrence theorem* of Poincaré. Its proof is very easy. Let W be a wandering set. Then the sets $T^{-1}W$, $T^{-2}W$, $T^{-3}W$, ... are pairwise disjoint. Therefore for any $N \geq 1$ we find the inequality

$$P(\bigcup_{j=1}^{N} T^{-j}W) = \sum_{j=1}^{N} P(T^{-j}W) = NP(W) \leq P(X).$$

Hence $P(W) = 0$.

The result is not true for σ-finite measures. Just take the map $Tx = x + 1$ on the real axis $\mathbb{R}$ and the Lebesgue measure λ.

The most important result for maps $T : X \to X$ with an invariant measure P is the *(individual) ergodic theorem*. If f is integrable then

$$\lim_{N \to \infty} \frac{1}{N} \sum_{j=0}^{N-1} f(T^j x) = f^*(x)$$

almost everywhere. If P is a finite measure then

$$\int_X f^* dP = \int_X f dP.$$

If P is σ-finite but not finite then $f^*(x) = 0$ almost everywhere. Furthermore $f^*(Tx) = f^*(x)$ almost everywhere.

The real difficult part is the prof of convergence. Beside of convergence almost everywhere there are so-called *mean ergodic theorems*. Convergence almost everywhere is replaced by convergence in a suitable L^p-space. This is a set of functions with the norm $\|f\|_p = \sqrt[p]{\int_X |f(x)|^p dP(x)}$. The first proofs were given for invertible maps T. A real progress was made when the *maximal ergodic theorem* was used as an essential tool. The development of ergodic theory can be seen by comparing the classics [Hopf 1937] and [Jacobs 1960] with the many newer literature.

We show some applications of ergodic theory to the typical f-expansions $Tx = 2x - \lfloor 2x \rfloor$ and $Tx = \frac{1}{x} - \lfloor \frac{1}{x} \rfloor$. Both maps are ergodic and admit an invariant measure which is *equivalent* to Lebesgue measure. This is Lebsgue measure λ in the first example and the measure μ with density

$$\frac{d\mu}{d\lambda}(x) = \frac{1}{(1+x)\log 2}$$

for continued fractions.

The main question is about the average appearance of a given block of digits $(\varepsilon_1, \varepsilon_2, ..., \varepsilon_s)$. This block appears in the expansion of x at place n exactly if $T^{n-1}x \in B(\varepsilon_1, \varepsilon_2, ..., \varepsilon_s)$. If $A(N, \varepsilon_1, \varepsilon_2, ..., \varepsilon_s; x)$ is the number of appearances for $0 \leq n < N$ then taking ϕ as the indicator function of the cylinder $B(\varepsilon_1, \varepsilon_2, ..., \varepsilon_s)$ we find that

$$\lim_{N \to \infty} \frac{A(N, \varepsilon_1, \varepsilon_2, ..., \varepsilon_s; x)}{N} = \lim_{N \to \infty} \sum_{j=0}^{N-1} \phi(T^j x)$$

$$= \int_0^1 \phi \, d\mu = \mu(B(\varepsilon_1, \varepsilon_2, ..., \varepsilon_s))$$

holds for almost all $x \in [0,1]$. For dyadic expansions we find

$$\mu(B(\varepsilon_1, \varepsilon_2, ..., \varepsilon_s)) = 2^{-s}$$

and for continued fractions

$$\mu(B(\varepsilon_1, \varepsilon_2, ..., \varepsilon_s)) = \frac{1}{\log 2} \left| \int_{\frac{p_s}{q_s}}^{\frac{p_s + p_{s+1}}{q_s + q_{s+1}}} \frac{dx}{1+x} \right|.$$

From this result it is easy to see that for a given f-expansion almost all numbers $x \in [0,1]$ contain every block with the calculated probability. For $g = 2$ such a number is called *normal* with respect to base 2 (normal numbers were already mentioned in the chapter Around the theorem of Borel and Bernstein). It is evident that a similar result holds for all integral bases $g \geq 2$. Since there are only countably many blocks and countably many bases almost all numbers are normal with respect to any basis. They are called *absolutely normal*. However, [Schmidt 1960] and [Cassels 1959] showed that there are infinitely many numbers $x \in [0,1]$ which are normal to base 2 but not normal to base 3 and vice versa. A similar story holds if one compares normality to base 2 and normality with respect to continued fraction expansion [Kraaikamp & Nakada 2001] (see also [Kraaikamp & Nakada 2000]).

We mention another application to continued fractions. One proves by induction

$$\frac{1}{q_n + q_{n-1}y} = x \cdot Tx \cdot ... \cdot T^{n-1}x, \ y = T^n y.$$

Therefore

$$-\sum_{j=0}^{n-1} \log T^j x = \log(q_n + q_{n-1}y).$$

Since

$$\log q_n \leq \log(q_n + q_{n-1}y) < \log q_n + \log 2$$

we get for almost all x the relation

$$\lim_{n \to \infty} \left(-\frac{1}{n} \sum_{j=0}^{n-1} \log T^j x \right) = \lim_{n \to \infty} \frac{\log q_n}{n} = -\frac{1}{\log 2} \int_0^1 \frac{\log x}{1+x} dx.$$

Since

$$-\int_0^1 \frac{\log x}{1+x} dx = \int_0^1 \frac{\log(1+x)}{x} dx = \sum_{k=0}^{\infty} \int_0^1 \frac{x^k}{k+1} dx = \frac{\pi^2}{12}$$

we finally get

$$\lim_{n \to \infty} \frac{\log q_n(x)}{n} = \frac{\pi^2}{12}$$

almost everywhere.
Since

$$\frac{1}{q_n(q_n + q_{n+1})} \leq |x - \frac{p_n}{q_n}| \leq \frac{1}{q_n q_{n+1}}$$

we also obtain

$$\lim_{n \to \infty} \frac{1}{n} \log |x - \frac{p_n}{q_n}| = -\frac{\pi^2}{6 \log 2}$$

and

$$\lim_{n \to \infty} \log \lambda(B(k_1, k_2, ..., k_n)) = -\frac{\pi^2}{6 \log 2}$$

almost everywhere. The last result is connected with *entropy*.
It is clear from these examples that the application of ergodic theory provides a plenty of results. However, given an f-expansion some questions remain.
(1) Does the set of cylinders generate the σ-algebra of Borel sets?
For dimension $d = 1$ this is not so serious a problem because cylinders are in all known cases just intervals. If $d = 2$ cylinders may be triangles or quadrangles and one has to consider their diameters.
(2) Is the map which is related to an f-expansion ergodic?
In a more modern setting *conditional expectations* and the *martingale convergence theorem* are used (see e. g. [Billingsley 1965]). Let $\mathcal{G} \subseteq \mathcal{F}$ be a σ-subfield. A function $g = E\{f\|\mathcal{G}\}$ is called the conditional expectation of the integrable function f if
(i) the function $g = E\{f\|\mathcal{G}\}$ is measurable with respect to the given subfield which means that for any measurable set A the preimage $g^{-1}A \in \mathcal{G}$ and
(ii) $\int_M E\{f\|\mathcal{G}\} dP = \int_M f dP$ for all $M \in \mathcal{G}$.
If $\mathcal{G}_n$ is the σ-subfield generated by all cylinders of rank n and if $A \in \mathcal{G}_n$ then for $x \in A$

$$g(x) = \frac{1}{P(A)} \int_A f dP.$$

The main result is as follows. If $\mathcal{G}$ is the smallest σ-algebra which contains an increasing sequence $\mathcal{G}_n$ of subfields then

$$\lim_{n \to \infty} E\{f \| \mathcal{G}_n\} = E\{f \| \mathcal{G}\}$$

almost everywhere. If $\mathcal{G} = \mathcal{F}$ then clearly $E\{f \| \mathcal{G}\} = f$. Now suppose that the cylinders generate the Borel field. If f is the indicator function of a set A (i.e. $c_A(x) = 1$ if $x \in A$ and $c_A(x) = 0$ else) and $\mathcal{G}_n$ is the subfield generated by the cylinders of rank $\leq n$ then we obtain

$$\frac{1}{\lambda(B(k_1, k_2, ..., k_n))} \int_{B(k_1, k_2, ..., k_n)} c_A(x) d\lambda(x) \to c_A(x)$$

holds for almost all x. If we look at an invariant set $A = T^{-1}A$ we discover the ideas of Knopp and others.

(3) Does an invariant measure μ exist which is *absolutely continuous* with respect to the given measure P? This means that $P(E) = 0$ implies $\mu(E) = 0$. If such a measure exists the *Theorem of Radon and Nikodym* implies that

$$\mu(E) = \int_E h(x) dP(x)$$

for a *density function* h. If the map T is ergodic and μ is a finite measure then it is unique up to a multiplicative constant. If μ is σ-finite (and not finite) the additional condition that T is *conservative* is needed to ensure uniqueness.

Chapter 17

Invariant measures

One of the central issues of ergodic theory is the problem of *invariant measures*. Given a map $T : B \to B$ on a measure space $(B, \mathfrak{F})$ where $\mathfrak{F}$ is a σ-algebra of so-called *measurable sets* a measure μ is called an *invariant measure* if for any measurable set E the equality $\mu(T^{-1}E) = \mu(E)$ holds. Since measure spaces $(B, \mathfrak{F})$ which correspond to an f-expansion or more generally to a *fibred system* are isomorphic to a subspace of a *shift* the mere existence of such a measure is clear. The question is the following. Given a measure λ on $(B, \mathfrak{F})$ does there exist an invariant measure μ which is *absolutely continuous* with respect to λ, i. e. if $\lambda(E) = 0$ then $\mu(E) = 0$ should follow. Before discussing the existence of such measures we will look at some examples. If μ is absolutely continuous the famous Theorem of Radon and Nikodym (which can be found in any good book on measure theory, e. g. the real classic book [Halmos 1950]) implies that there is a *density*, i. e. a function $h = h(x)$ such that

$$\mu(E) = \int_E h d\lambda.$$

An important tool is the *transfer operator* A defined by the equation

$$\int_{T^{-1}E} f d\lambda = \int (Af) d\lambda.$$

Its existence is also insured by the Theorem of Radon and Nikodym. One sees that h is the density of an invariant measure if and only if $Ah = h$ holds. This equation is known as the *Kuzmin equation* or *transfer equation*.

(1) g-adic maps, $g \geq 2$, $\ Tx = gx - \lfloor gx \rfloor$

$$h(x) = \sum_{j=0}^{g-1} h\left(\frac{x+j}{g}\right)\frac{1}{g}.$$

It is immediately clear that $h(x) \equiv 1$ is a solution and the Lebesgue measure is invariant.

(2) Regular continued fractions, $\ Tx = \frac{1}{x} - \lfloor \frac{1}{x} \rfloor$

$$h(x) = \sum_{j=1}^{\infty} h\left(\frac{1}{x+j}\right)\frac{1}{(x+j)^2}.$$

From an old conjecture of Gauss (see [Gauss 1812]) we know that $h(x) = \frac{1}{1+x}$ is a solution. Therefore the function

$$h(x) = \frac{1}{\log 2(1+x)}$$

is the density of a probability measure. The question arises how to find the solution. Some kind of guess work could help. Suppose that $h(x)$ is also defined outside the unit interval. The equation

$$h(x) = \sum_{j=1}^{\infty} h\left(\frac{1}{x+j}\right)\frac{1}{(x+j)^2}$$

implies

$$h(x+1) = \sum_{j=2}^{\infty} h\left(\frac{1}{x+j}\right)\frac{1}{(x+j)^2}.$$

Therefore

$$h(x) - h(x+1) = h\left(\frac{1}{x+1}\right)\frac{1}{(x+1)^2}.$$

Maybe you see that $h(x) = \frac{1}{x+1}$ is a solution for the last equation.

(3) $Tx = \frac{x}{1-x} - \lfloor \frac{x}{1-x} \rfloor$
This is the f-expansion for $f(x) = \frac{x}{1+x}$. The Kuzmin equation is

$$h(x) = \sum_{j=1}^{\infty} h\left(\frac{x}{1+jx}\right)\frac{1}{(1+jx)^2}.$$

In this case $h(x) = \frac{1}{x}$ is a solution but note that this function is not integrable on the interval $[0,1]$. This measure μ is σ-*finite* because $]0,1] = \bigcup_n [\frac{1}{n+1}, \frac{1}{n}]$ and $\mu([\frac{1}{n+1}, \frac{1}{n}]) = \log(n+1) - \log n$. The letter σ stands for a countable family of disjoint subsets which was called a sum in older days.

(4) A similar case is $Tx = \tan x$. The Kuzmin equation reads

$$h(x) = \sum_{j=-\infty}^{\infty} h(\arctan x + j\pi) \frac{1}{1+x^2}.$$

Surprisingly $h(x) = \frac{1}{x^2}$ is a solution! In the theory of complex variables one of the foremost examples of a Mittag-Leffler series is

$$\sum_{j \to -\infty}^{\infty} \frac{1}{(z+j)^2} = \left(\frac{\pi}{\sin \pi z}\right)^2.$$

If one substitutes $\pi z = \arctan x$ we obtain the above equation.

(5) The *quadratic map* $Tx = 4x(1-x)$ is the easiest example of the so-called *quadratic family* $p(a; x) = ax(1-x)$ with parameter a which is one of the gates to chaos theory. For $a = 4$ one has to solve the equation

$$h(x) = h\left(\frac{1 - \sqrt{1-x}}{2}\right) \frac{1}{4\sqrt{1-x}} + h\left(\frac{1 + \sqrt{1-x}}{2}\right) \frac{1}{4\sqrt{1-x}}.$$

An elementary calculation shows that

$$h(x) = \frac{1}{\sqrt{x(1-x)}}$$

is the desired density. This is the density of the so-called *equilibrium measure* in the sense of potential theory (see e. g. [Tsuji 1975]). If one introduces $T^*x = (\alpha \circ T \circ \alpha^{-1})x$ with $\alpha(x) = \frac{2}{\pi} \arcsin \sqrt{x}$ we obtain

$$T^*x = 2x, \ 0 \le x \le \frac{1}{2}, \ T^*x = 2 - 2x, \ \frac{1}{2} \le x \le 1.$$

It is obvious that Lebesgue measure is invariant for the map T^*. Therefore

$$h(x) = \alpha'(x) = \frac{1}{\pi\sqrt{x(1-x)}}.$$

If $\beta(y) = \sin^2 \frac{\pi y}{2}$ is the inverse function to α, then the relation

$$\beta \circ T^* = T \circ \beta$$

is the well known identity $\sin 2t = 2 \sin t \cos t$ with $t = \frac{\pi y}{2}$.

(6) Interesting enough we also find a solution for $Tx = \sqrt{4x(1-x)}$. The Kuzmin equation is

$$h(x) = h\Big(\frac{1 - \sqrt{1 - x^2}}{2}\Big)\frac{x}{2\sqrt{1 - x^2}} + h\Big(\frac{1 + \sqrt{1 - x^2}}{2}\Big)\frac{x}{2\sqrt{1 - x^2}}.$$

A lengthy calculation shows that

$$h(x) = \frac{1}{2\sqrt{1 - x}}$$

is a solution.

(7) The so-called *Boole's transformation* [Adler & Weiss 1973] is given on $\mathbb{R} \setminus \{0\}$ as $Tx = x - \frac{1}{x}$. It is easy to see that Lebesgue measure is invariant! The equation

$$x = Ty = y - \frac{1}{y}$$

leads to the quadratic equation

$$y^2 - xy - 1$$

which has to real roots $y_1 = y_1(x)$ and $y_2 = y_2(x)$. Since

$$y_1(x) + y_2(x) = x$$

we obtain by differentiation

$$y_1'(x) + y_2'(x) = 1$$

which is the Kuzmin equation for $h(x) = 1$.

In fact there are numerous examples for which we can write down the invariant density using known functions. Just start with

$$Tx = 2x, \ 0 \le x < \frac{1}{2},$$

say. If $h(x) > 0$ is a density on the interval $[0, 1]$ with the condition $h(x) - \frac{1}{2}h(\frac{x}{2}) > 0$ one can find many examples of a map T which has $h(x)$ as its density. If $H(x)$ is the *distribution function* of $h(x)$, i. e. $H(x) = \int_0^x h(t)dt$, $V_0(x) = \frac{x}{2}$ and the unknown $V_1(x)$ are the two inverse branches of the desired T we obtain

$$H(x) = H(\frac{x}{2}) - H(0) + H(V_1(x)) - H(\frac{1}{2}).$$

Then

$$H(V_1(x)) = H(x) - H(\frac{x}{2}) + H(\frac{1}{2})$$

which gives

$$V_1(x) = H^{-1}(H(x) - H(\frac{x}{2}) + H(\frac{1}{2})).$$

Since $V_1(x)$ is differentiable and

$$h(V_1(x))V_1'(x) = h(x) - \frac{1}{2}h(\frac{x}{2}) > 0$$

we see that $V_1'(x) > 0$. Therefore V_1 is increasing and has an inverse on $[\frac{1}{2}, 1]$ which is the second branch of T.

However, no method is known to find an invariant density. We will discuss some sufficient conditions shortly but first we list some innocent looking examples for which we know that an invariant density exists but no description by known functions can be given up to now.

(1) Bolyai's map which is the f-expansion for

$$f(x) = \sqrt[m]{1+x} - 1, \ 0 \le x \le 2^m - 1.$$

We take $m = 2$. This is the map

$$Tx = x^2 + 2x, \ 0 \le x < \sqrt{2}$$

$$Tx = x^2 + 2x - 1, \ \sqrt{2} \le x < \sqrt{3}$$

$$Tx = x^2 + 2x - 2, \ \sqrt{3} \le x < 1.$$

The Kuzmin equation reads

$$h(x) = \frac{h(\sqrt{1+x} - 1) + h(\sqrt{2+x} - 1) + h(\sqrt{3+x} - 1)}{2\sqrt{1+x}}$$

but no explicit solution is known (for a lot of interesting results see [Jenkinson & Pollicott 2000]).

(2) Another example is the following modification of continued fractions [Dajani, Kraaikamp & Langeveld 2015].

$$Tx = \frac{a}{x} - (a^2 + j), \ \frac{1}{a^2 + j + 1} \leq x < \frac{1}{a^2 + j}, \ 0 \leq j < a, \ a = 1, 2, 3, \dots$$

The Kuzmin equation is given as

$$h(x) = \sum_{a=1}^{\infty} \sum_{j=0}^{a-1} h\left(\left(\frac{a}{a^2 + j + x}\right)\frac{a}{(a^2 + j + x)^2}\right).$$

Although an invariant density exists no explicit form has been found.

A great break-through happened around 1951 (see e. g. [Ryll-Nardzweski 1951]) when results of ergodic theory were applied to maps T which are related to f-expansions. One wonders why ergodic theory was applied so lately. Some prior attempts (e. g. [Doeblin & Fortet 1937] were not taken up further.

An important existence theorem for invariant measures reads as follows. If there is a constant $C \geq 1$ such that for all measurable sets E and every $n \geq 0$ the condition

$$C^{-1}\lambda(E) \leq \lambda(T^{-n}) \leq C\lambda(E)$$

holds then there exists an invariant measure μ such that

$$C^{-1}\lambda(E) \leq \mu(E) \leq C\lambda(E).$$

The proof is due to methods from Banach space theory [Dunford & Miller 1946]. Rényi in his classical paper on f-expansions [Rényi 1957] gives a sufficient condition for the theorem which applies to *convergent f-expansions*. Define

$$H_n(x, t) = \frac{df_n(\varepsilon_1(x), \dots, \varepsilon_{n-1}(x), \varepsilon_n(x) + t)}{dt}$$

for admissible sequences of digits $\varepsilon_1(x), \dots, \varepsilon_n(x)$ then he supposes

$$\sup_{0 < t < 1} H_n(x, t) \leq C \inf_{0 < t < 1} H_n(x, t).$$

$B(\varepsilon_1, \dots, \varepsilon_n) = \{x \in [0, 1] : \varepsilon_1(x) = \varepsilon_1, \dots, \varepsilon_n(x) = \varepsilon_n\}$ is the interval with endpoints $f_n(\varepsilon_1, \dots, \varepsilon_n)$ and $f_n(\varepsilon_1, \dots, \varepsilon_n + 1)$. Rényi supposes further that for $y \in]0,1[$ the function $f(\varepsilon_1, ..., \varepsilon_n + y)$ is defined and $f(\varepsilon_1, ..., \varepsilon_n + y) < 1$. This condition corresponds to the condition that all cylinders $B(\varepsilon)$ are *proper*.

If $[a,b] \subseteq]0,1[$ then

$$\lambda(T^{-n}[a,b]) \sum_{\varepsilon_1, ..., \varepsilon_n} |f_n(\varepsilon_1, ..., \varepsilon_n + b) - f_n(\varepsilon_1, ..., \varepsilon_n + a)|.$$

Since

$$|f_n(\varepsilon_1, ..., \varepsilon_n + b) - f_n(\varepsilon_1, ..., \varepsilon_n + a)| = H_n(x, \xi)(b - a)$$

we find

$$\sum_{\varepsilon_1, ..., \varepsilon_n} \inf_{0 < t < 1} H_n(x, t) \le \frac{T^{-n}[a,b]}{b - a} \le \sum_{\varepsilon_1, ..., \varepsilon_n} \sup_{0 < t < 1} H_n(x, t).$$

Therefore $C^{-1}\lambda(E) \le \lambda(T^{-n}E) \le C\lambda(E)$ if $E = [a,b]$ but standard methods of measure theory imply that this true for all measurable sets E.

In the case of β-expansions, namely for $f(x) = \frac{x}{\beta}$ it is not true that for alll values y, $0 < y < 1$ the condition $f(\varepsilon_1, ..., \varepsilon_n + y) < 1$ is satisfied. Take $\beta = \frac{1+\sqrt{5}}{2}$, $\varepsilon_1 = 1$ then

$$f(1 + y) = \frac{1 + y}{\beta} < 1$$

only for $y < \beta - 1 = \frac{1}{\beta}$. Here Rényi circumvents this difficulty as follows. Clearly

$$\sum_{n=1}^{\infty} \frac{\lfloor \beta \rfloor}{\beta^n} = \frac{\lfloor \beta \rfloor}{\beta - 1} < 1.$$

Therefore there exists a value N such that

$$\sum_{n=1}^{N} \frac{\lfloor \beta \rfloor}{\beta^n} > 1.$$

Let $S(n)$ be the number of *canonical (= admissible) sequences* and put $S(0) = 1$. If the block $(\varepsilon_1, ..., \varepsilon_{n-1})$ is canonical then there is $k = k(\varepsilon_1, ..., \varepsilon_{n-1})$ such that $(\varepsilon_1, ..., \varepsilon_{n-1}, \varepsilon_n)$ is canonical for $0 \le \varepsilon_n \le k$ but not for $\varepsilon_n > k$. For different sequences $(\varepsilon_1, ..., \varepsilon_{n-1})$ the intervals

$$[\frac{\varepsilon_1}{\beta} + \frac{\varepsilon_2}{\beta^2} + ... + \frac{\varepsilon_{n-1}}{\beta^{n-1}}, \frac{\varepsilon_1}{\beta} + \frac{\varepsilon_2}{\beta^2} + ... + \frac{\varepsilon_{n-1}}{\beta^{n-1}} + \frac{k}{\beta^n}[$$

are disjoint and therefore

$$\frac{S(n) - S(n-1)}{\beta^n} = \frac{1}{\beta^n} \sum_{\varepsilon_1, \dots, \varepsilon_{n-1}} k(\varepsilon_1, \dots, \varepsilon_{n-1}) \le 1$$

$$S(n) - S(n-1) \le \beta^n$$

which gives

$$S(n) \le \frac{\beta^{n-1}}{\beta - 1}, \, n \ge 1.$$

Note that $(\varepsilon_1, \dots, \varepsilon_{n-1})$ is canonical if and only if $(\varepsilon_1, \dots, \varepsilon_{n-1}, 0)$ is canonical. Therefore $S(n) - S(n-1)$ is the number of all canonical blocks $(\varepsilon_1, \dots, \varepsilon_{n-1}, \varepsilon_n)$ for which $\varepsilon_n \neq 0$. Since the distance of two numbers $\frac{\varepsilon_1}{\beta} + \frac{\varepsilon_2}{\beta^2} + \dots + \frac{\varepsilon_n}{\beta^n}$ is $\le \frac{1}{\beta^n}$ we get $S(n) \ge \beta^n$. A side product is $\lim_{n \to \infty} \sqrt[n]{S(n)} = \beta$. As $T^{-n}E$ consists of $S(n)$ sets each of which has a measure not exceeding $\frac{1}{\beta^n}$ we have

$$\lambda(T^{-n}E) \le \frac{S(n)\lambda(E)}{\beta^n} \le \frac{\beta}{\beta - 1}\lambda(E).$$

On the other hand $S(n) - S(n-1)$ of the sets mentioned before have the measure equal $\frac{\lambda(E)}{\beta^n}$. Therefore we obtain

$$\lambda(T^{-n}E) \ge \frac{S(n) - S(n-1)}{\beta^n}\lambda(E).$$

Then

$$\frac{1}{n}\sum_{k=0}^{n-1} \lambda(T^{-k}E) \ge \frac{1}{n}(1 + \sum_{k=1}^{n-1} \frac{S(k) - S(k-1)}{\beta^k})\lambda(E).$$

The estimate

$$\beta^k \le S(k) \le \frac{\beta^{k+1}}{\beta - 1}$$

then gives the result

$$\frac{1}{n}\sum_{k=0}^{n-1} \lambda(T^{-k}E) \ge \frac{\beta - 1}{\beta}\lambda(E).$$

We now can apply again the result of Dunford and Miller. In the example $\beta = \frac{1+\sqrt{5}}{2}$ one finds

$$h(x) = \frac{5 + 3\sqrt{5}}{10}, \, 0 \le x < \frac{-1 + \sqrt{5}}{2}$$

$$h(x) = \frac{5 + \sqrt{5}}{10}, \quad \frac{-1 + \sqrt{5}}{2} \le x < 1.$$

We formulate a generalization of Rényi's ideas. Let $T : B \to B$ be a map on a fibred system with the following conditions

(a) $\lambda(B) = 1$

(b) All cylinders of the time-1-partition are full, i. e. $TB(k) = B$.

(c) There is a constant $C \ge 1$ such that

$$\sup_{y \in B} \omega(k_1, .., k_s; y) \le C \inf_{y \in B} \omega(k_1, ..., k_s; y).$$

(d) The cylinders generate the σ-algebra of Borel sets.

Then there exists a unique invariant probability measure μ such that

$$C^{-1}\lambda(E) \le \mu(E) \le C\lambda(E).$$

We remember that $V(k_1, ..., k_s)$ denotes the inverse map of T^s restricted to the cylinder $B(k_1, ..., k_s)$ and $\omega(k_1, ..., k_s)$ its Jacobian defined by

$$\int_E \omega(k_1, ..., k_s)d\lambda = \lambda(T^{-s}E \cap B(k_1, ..., k_s)).$$

By condition (d) it is sufficient to consider cylinders $E = B(k_1, ..., k_s)$. Then

$$T^{-n}E = \bigcup_{a_1,...,a_n} B(a_1, ..., a_n, k_1, ..., k_s).$$

Hence we calculate

$$\lambda(T^{-n}E) = \sum_{a_1,...,a_n} \lambda(B(a_1, ..., a_n, k_1, ..., k_s))$$

$$= \sum_{a_1,...,a_n} \int_B \omega(a_1, ..., a_n, k_1, ..., k_s; y)dy$$

$$= \sum_{a_1,...,a_n} \int_B \omega(a_1, ..., a_n; V(k_1, ..., k_s)y)\omega(k_1, ..., k_s; y)dy$$

$$\le C\lambda(B(k_1, ..., k_s)) \sum_{a_1,...,a_n} \lambda(B(a_1, ..., a_n)) = C\lambda(E).$$

In a similar way we obtain

$$\lambda(T^{-n}E) \geq \frac{1}{C}\lambda(E).$$

For dimension $d = 1$ condition (c) can be ensured by the "folklore theorem"(see the chapter Measure zero or one). For f-expansions condition (d) is ensured by its convergence (called *validity*).

The condition $\lambda(T^{-n}E) \leq C\lambda(E)$ sounds very natural. However the proof for the existence of an invariant measure μ uses the *Banach-Mazur limit*. The Banach-Mazur limit is a *linear functional* (see any good book on functional analysis) which we denote by Lim_n. It is defined on the space of all bounded sequences $l^\infty = \{(a_n) : \sup_n |a_n| < \infty\}$. It satisfies the conditions

(I) $\mathrm{Lim}_n(\alpha a_n + \beta b_n) = \alpha\mathrm{Lim}_n a_n + \beta\mathrm{Lim}_n b_n$.

(II) $\mathrm{Lim}_n a_{n+1} = \mathrm{Lim}_n a_n$.

(III) $\liminf_n a_n \leq \mathrm{Lim}_n a_n \leq \limsup_n a_n$.

Clearly, if the sequence (a_n) is convergent then $\mathrm{Lim}_n a_n = \lim_{n\to\infty} a_n$. This functional was introduced by Stefan Banach in his book [Banach 1932].

Although Khintchine has played an important role in the development of ergodic theory ([Khintchine 1932]; see e. g. [von Plato 1994]) he did not apply ergodic theory to continued fractions or other f-expansions. The reason for this can only be guessed. Ergodic theory in mathematics was applied to *flows* and invertible maps first (see [Hopf 1937]). A flow is a family of maps $T_t : X \to X$, $t \in \mathbb{R}$ (t stands for time or Latin *tempus*) with the condition $T_t \circ T_s = T_{t+s}$. Therefore we also have $T_t \circ T_{-t} = \mathbf{1}$. The maps associated with f-expansions and fibred systems are not invertible. In fact, the ergodic theorem is true for *nonsingular* measurable maps $T : X \to X$. The concept "nonsingular" means that $\lambda(E) = 0$ implies $\lambda(T^{-1}E) = 0$. In fact, S. Hartman, E. Marczewski and C. Ryll-Nardzewski made the application of ergodic theory to f-expansions popular [Hartman & Marczewski & Ryll-Nardzewski 1951]. We mention some more results which were applied to f-expansions. A by now classical paper is [Lasota & Yorke 1973]. On similar lines are e. g. [Wagner 1979] and [Alufohai 1981]. He considers piecewise monotonic

maps of the unit interval $I = [0, 1]$ onto itself. The following assumptions
are made. There is a partition $\{P_1, ..., P_L\}$ of $[0, 1]$ into intervals such that
T maps the interval P_j onto an interval Q_j and T is strictly monotone and
absolutely continuous on the interior of P_j. Without loss of generality
one may assume that either $Q_j \cap Q_i = \emptyset$ Or $Q_j = Q_i$. Furthermore some
conditions on the inverse branches $V_j : Q_j \to P_j$ are required. The main
result is the decomposition of I into *forward invariant sets* (this means
$TE = E$) $A_1, ..., A_s$ such that on each A_p there is an invariant measure μ_p
which is equivalent to λ 0n A_p. This means that $\mu_p(E) = \mu_p(T^{-1}E \cap A_p)$.
Furthermore the restriction of T to A_p is ergodic. The sets $A_1, ..., A_s$ are
called *ergodic components*.

If T arises from an f-expansion then there is only one ergodic component.
The example

$$Tx = \frac{6x + 2}{5} \text{ for } 0 \leq x < \frac{1}{2}$$

$$Tx = \frac{6x - 3}{5} \text{ for } \frac{1}{2} \leq x < 1$$

shows that T is not an *exact transformation* (this notion will be shortly
dealt in the chapter on *entropy*) .

Chapter 18

More ideas on invariant measures

Here we mention some ideas which were developed to find an invariant measure or in some cases even an explicit form (comparable with $h(x) = \frac{1}{1+x}$ for continued fractions) for the invariant density. These ideas were also used to prove ergodicity.

Use of a *conjugate* fibred system. Let (B, T) and (B^*, T^*) be fibred systems. These systems are conjugate if there is a bijective map $\alpha : B \to B^*$ such that $T^*(\alpha(x)) = \alpha(T(x))$. If μ^* is an invariant measure for T^* then the measure defined by $\mu(E) = \mu^*(\alpha E)$ is invariant for the map T. Using densities this is written as

$$h(x) = h^*(\alpha(x)) \Big| \frac{\partial \alpha}{\partial x} \Big|.$$

A famous example are the Chebyshev polynomials [Adler & Rivlin 1964]. Let $T_n(x) = \cos(n \arccos x)$ then the map $\alpha(x) = \frac{1}{\pi} \arccos x$ turns T_n on $B = [-1, 1]$ into a fibred system with piecewise linear branches. Therefore $h^*(x) \equiv 1$ and we obtain

$$h(x) = |\alpha'(x)| = \frac{1}{\pi \sqrt{1 - x^2}}.$$

Use of an *auxiliary measure* (which is equivalent to the use of a suitable

131

conjugacy). We replace Lebesgue measure by an equiavalent one, i. e.

$$\nu(E) = \int_E g(x)d\lambda(x), \, g(x) > 0.$$

Then for the one-dimensional case

$$\alpha(x) = \int_0^x g(t)dt$$

is a suitable conjugacy. In [Bowen 1979] this method is applied to the map

$$Tx = 1 - 2|x|^\gamma, \, \gamma > 1, \, -1 \le x \le 1.$$

Since $\lim_{x \to 0} |T'(x)| = 0$ there is no hope for Rényi's condition. But one can use the function

$$g(x) = (1 - |t|^\gamma)^{\frac{1}{\gamma - 1}}.$$

It is not necessary to calculate T^* explicitly but it is tedious to prove that T^* satisfies Adler's conditions. The key is the following observation. If

$$\nu(T^{-s}E \cap B(k_1, ..., k_s)) = \int_E \psi(k_1, ..., k_s; x)g(x)dx$$

then

$$\psi(k; x) = \omega(k; x)\frac{g(V(k)x)}{g(x)}.$$

More details can be found in [Reichssöllner 1989].

First return map The concept of first return map (or induced transformation) dates back to the days of Poincaré and has been widely used in ergodic theory (see [Bowen 1979] which contains an afterword by Roy L. Adler and additional comments by Caroline Series, and [Pianigiani 1980]). The idea is to consider a map on a suitable subset. If there is an invariant measure on this subset one can expand it to an invariant measure on B. Let $T : B \to B$ be given. The set $A \subseteq B$ satisfies

$$\text{(a)} \qquad A \subseteq \bigcup_{n=1}^\infty T^{-n}A \text{ mod } 0$$

$$\text{(b)} \qquad \lambda(A) < \infty \quad \text{or} \quad \lambda(B \setminus A) < \infty.$$

Then the *first return time* is defined almost everywhere on A as

$$n(x) := \min\{n \ge 1 : T^n x \in A\}.$$

Then the map $R : A \to A$ is a.e. defined as

$$R(x) := T^{n(x)}x.$$

This is called the first return map (or induced transformation). Assume that μ is an invariant measure for R. Now let

$$C_n = \{x \in A : n(x) \geq n\}$$

then

$$\lambda(E) = \sum_{n=1}^{\infty} \mu(C_n \cap T^{-n}E)$$

is an invariant measure for T.

Jump transformation This device is explained in [Schweiger 1995]. This idea will be outlined with β-expansions.

We consider the f-expansion with $f(x) = \frac{x}{\beta}$, $\beta > 1$, non-integral. Then the cylinders $B(\varepsilon) = [\frac{\varepsilon}{\beta}, \frac{\varepsilon+1}{\beta}[$ are full, i.e. $TB(\varepsilon) = [0,1[$ if $\varepsilon < \lfloor\beta\rfloor - 1$ but the right-most cylinder

$$D_1 = [\frac{\lfloor\beta\rfloor - 1}{\beta}, \frac{1}{\beta}[$$

is not mapped fully onto $[0,1[$. If one considers the iterates $T^2, T^3, \dots$ then one sees there is at most one right-most interval D_n which is not mapped fully under T^n onto $[0,1[$. The jump transformation S is defined as

$$Rx = Tx, \ x \in B \setminus D_1$$

$$Rx = T^2x, \ x \in D_1 \setminus D_2$$

$$\dots$$

$$Rx = T^nx, \ x \in D_{n-1} \setminus D_n$$

$$\dots$$

Since Lebesgue measure λ is invariant for R the measure

$$\mu(E) = \sum_{n=0}^{\infty} \lambda(T^{-n}E \cap D_n)$$

is invariant for T. Taking densities we find the Parry-Gel'fond formula

$$h(x) = \sum_{x < T^n 1} \beta^{-n}.$$

Dual (or backward) algorithm The main observation is the following. If you look at the continued fraction of a number $x \in [0,1]$

$$x = \cfrac{1}{a_1 + \cfrac{1}{a_2 + ... + \cfrac{1}{a_n + ...}}}$$

then one also has

$$\frac{q_{n-1}}{q_n} = \cfrac{1}{a_n + \cfrac{1}{a_{n-1} + ... + \cfrac{1}{a_1}}}.$$

This is a finite continued fraction in the reverse order.

The idea of a dual algorithm seems to go back to [Nakada & Ito & Tanaka 1977]. The fibred system $(B^{\#}, T^{\#})$ is called a dual fibred system (or a backward algorithm) with respect to (B, T) if the following condition holds: $(k_1, k_2, \ldots, k_n)$ is an admissible block of digits for T (see 1.2.2(a)) if and only if $(k_n, \ldots, k_2, k_1)$ is an admissible block of digits for $T^{\#}$. As usual $V(k)$ denotes the inverse branches of T having Jacobians $\omega(k)$ with respect to a given measure λ. In an obvious notation we put $V^{\#}(k_n, \ldots, k_1)$ for the inverse branches of $T^{\#}$ and $\omega^{\#}(k_n, \ldots, k_1)$ for the Jacobians with respect to a given measure $\lambda^{\#}$. In most cases $\lambda = \lambda^{\#}$ is just Lebesgue measure. A measurable function $K(x, y) \geq 0$ is called a *kernel* if

$$K(x, V^{\#}(k)y)\omega^{\#}(k; y) = K(V(k)x, y)\omega(k; x)$$

for $x \in TB(k)$, $y \in T^{\#}B^{\#}(k)$ and $k \in I$. Let us assume first that all cylinders are full then it is easy to see that the integral

$$h(x) = \int_{B^{\#}} K(x, y) d\lambda^{\#}(y)$$

defines a T-invariant density. Let us apply this to continued fractions. Here $B = B^{\#} = [0, 1]$, $T = T^{\#}$, where $Tx = \frac{1}{x} - \lfloor \frac{1}{x} \rfloor$. Then

$$K(x, y) = \frac{1}{(1 + xy)^2}$$

is a good choice! Clearly we find again

$$h(x) = \frac{1}{1 + x} = \int_0^1 \frac{dy}{(1 + xy)^2}.$$

Two difficulties arise. First, one has to find a suitable kernel. In almost all 1-dimensional examples the kernel is given as

$$K(x,y) = \frac{1}{(1+xy)^2}.$$

If

$$V(k)x = \frac{C_k + D_k x)}{A_k + B_k x}$$

is a branch of the algorithm then

$$V^\# y = \frac{B_k + D_k y}{A_k + C_k y}$$

is a possible branch of the dual algorithm. But the second difficulty is the question if all the branches $V^\#$ fit together to form a suitable fibred system on an interval or a union of intervals. Very often a set of Cantor type seems to appear.

A special case is the following. There is a map $\varphi : B \to B^\#$ such that $\varphi \circ T = T^\# \circ \varphi$. This is assured if there is a matrix

$$\varphi = \begin{pmatrix} \alpha & \beta \\ \beta & \gamma \end{pmatrix}$$

such that for all $k \in I$ the equation

$$\begin{pmatrix} \alpha & \beta \\ \beta & \gamma \end{pmatrix} \begin{pmatrix} A_k & B_k \\ C_k & D_k \end{pmatrix} = \begin{pmatrix} A_k & C_k \\ B_k & D_k \end{pmatrix} \begin{pmatrix} \alpha & \beta \\ \beta & \gamma \end{pmatrix}$$

holds.

We give just one example. Let $f(x) = \frac{x}{\alpha+x}$, $\alpha \geq 1$, then

$$Tx = \frac{\alpha x}{1-x} - k, \ k = 0, 1, 2, \dots.$$

The dual map on the interval $[0, \frac{1}{\alpha-1}[$ is

$$T^\# y = \frac{-1 + (k+\alpha)y}{1 - ky}, \ k = 0, 1, 2, \dots.$$

The function ϕ is

$$\phi(t) = \frac{1-t}{\alpha - 1 + t}.$$

We already mentioned that invariant measures can be *σ-finite* but must not be finite. This means that B is a union of sets $X_1, X_2, X_3, \dots$ such that $\mu(X_j) < \infty$ but $\mu(B) = \infty$. The case $\alpha = 1$ in our example gives a σ-finite measure. For the interested reader we refer to [Thaler 1980, 1983, 2002] and [Aaronson 1997].

Chapter 19

Entropy

Since a digit can be regarded as a *random variable* the sequence of digits can be seen as the outcome of a *stochastic process*. This viewpoint is used e. g. in [Ibragimov & Linnik & Petrov 1971]. It has been fruitful to investigate the validity of *limit laws* and *mixing properties* (see e. g. [Philipp 1975/76, 1970, 1969, 1967] and [Philipp & Stackelberg 1969], to name but a few). A map T is called (*strongly*) *mixing* if for all measurable sets A and B the relation

$$\lim_{n \to \infty} \mu(A \cap T^{-n}B) = \mu(A)\mu(B)$$

holds. Clearly one is interested in the rate of mixing (sometimes called *rate of decay*), namely an upper bound for

$$|\mu(A \cap T^{-n}B) - \mu(A)\mu(B)|.$$

Another important idea is the concept of an *exact endomorphism* [Rohlin 1961]. Let $\mathcal{B}$ be the $\sigma-$algebra of measurable sets and $T^{-1}\mathcal{B}$ the σ-algebra of the preimages. Then T is called an exact endomorphism if

$$\bigcap_{j=0}^{\infty} T^{-j}\mathcal{B}$$

is "trivial". It contains only sets of measure 0 or 1. An exact endomorphism is strongly mixing.

Entropy is a central notion in ergodic theory. The concepts comes from thermodynamics. The word which comes from Greek $\varepsilon \nu \tau \rho \varepsilon \pi \omega$ 'to turn, change' describes the observation that in some sense thermodynamic processes are not reversible. A certain quantity, the entropy S grows during the process. The Second Law of Thermodynamics states that S is a non-decreasing function. This was found by Clausius and Kelvin around 1850. Boltzmann later connected the entropy of a system with the "thermodynamic probability" W of a state by his famous equation

$$S = k \log W$$

where k is a universal constant.

Shannon, one of the inventors of coding theory, used entropy as a measure of information. In his paper "Communication Theory - Exposition of Fundamentals"(*IRE Transactions Information Theory*, No. 1 pp, 105-107) he says: "In general, when there are a number of possible events or messages that may occur, there will also be a set of *a priori* probabilities for these messages and the amount of information, still arguing heuristically, should depend upon these probabilities. If one particular message is overwhelmingly probable, the amount of information or the *a priori* uncertainty will be small. It turns out that the appropriate measure for the amount of information when a choice is made from a set of possibilities with the probabilities $p_1, p_2, ..., p_n$ is given by the formula

$$H = -\sum_{i=1}^{n} p_i \log p_i. \quad (1)$$

...

Equation (1) is identical in form with certain formulas for entropy used in statistical mechanics, in particular in the formulation due to Boltzmann." (reprinted in [Sloane & Wyner, eds 1993:173]).

The number

$$H = -\sum_{i=1}^{n} p_i \log p_i$$

is therefore called the entropy. Note that if $p_1 = p_2 = ... = p_n$ then this number attains its maximum, namely $\log n$. Obviously this case can be seen as the "most random ". For sake of completeness we use the definition $0 \log 0 = \lim_{t \to 0+} t \log t = 0$.

Assume that you have to guess a number with at most four places, $x = e_3 e_2 e_1 e_0$, $e_3, e_2, e_1, e_0 \in \{0, 1, 2, .., 9\}$. Then you need at most

10^4 questions because there are 10 possibilities for each place. The number $\log 10^4 = 4 \log 10$ can be seen as a measure of information, In the digital area it became common to use the logarithm to base 2, i.e.

$$\mathrm{ld}\,\alpha = \frac{\log \alpha}{\log 2}.$$

then the entropy of a number with at most N places, $x = e_{N-1}e_{N-2}...e_1e_0$, $e_{N-1}, e_{N-2}, ..., e_1, e_0 \in \{0,1\}$ is just $\mathrm{ld}\,2^N = N$. Billingsley expresses it shortly: Uncertainty and information are related by the "formula" *information gained = uncertainty removed* [Billingsley 1965:62].

We will first present entropy as a kind of average for the size of the cylinders of an f-expansion (more general of a fibred system). We first consider g-adic expansions. Given a cylinder

$$B(\varepsilon_1, ..., \varepsilon_n) = \{x : \varepsilon_1(x) = \varepsilon_1, ..., \varepsilon_n(x) = \varepsilon_n\}$$

then its length is constant for a given n, namely

$$\lambda(B(\varepsilon_1, ..., \varepsilon_n)) = \frac{1}{g^n}.$$

One calls

$$-\frac{\log \lambda(B(\varepsilon_1, ..., \varepsilon_n))}{n} = \log g$$

the entropy of the g-adic expansion. We now consider regular continued fractions. Here

$$B(k_1, ..., k_n)) = \{x : k_1(x) = k_1, ..., k_n(x) = k_n\}$$

is an interval with endpoints $\frac{p_n}{q_n}$ and $\frac{p_n+p_{n-1}}{q_n+q_{n-1}}$. Its length is given by

$$\lambda(B(k_1, ..., k_n)) = \frac{1}{q_n(q_n + q_{n-1})}$$

which is not constant!

But the ergodic theorem allows us to prove that the limit

$$-\lim_{n\to\infty} \frac{\log \lambda(B(k_1, ..., k_n))}{n}$$

exists for almost all numbers $x \in [0, 1]$.

The relation

$$x \cdot Tx \cdot ... \cdot T^{n-1}x = \frac{1}{q_n + q_{n-1}T^n x}$$

can be easily proved by induction (note $a_1 = q_1$, $1 = q_0$). Then

$$\lambda(B(k_1, ..., k_n)) = \int_0^1 \frac{dy}{(q_n + q_{n-1}y)^2}$$

and

$$\frac{1}{4q_n^2} \leq \int_0^1 \frac{dy}{(q_n + q_{n-1}y)^2} \leq \frac{1}{q_n^2}.$$

Hence

$$-\frac{1}{n} \sum_{j=0}^{n-1} \log T^j x = \frac{\log(q_n + q_{n-1}T^n x)}{n} \sim \frac{\log q_n}{n}.$$

The ergodic theorem shows that

$$-\lim_{n \to \infty} \frac{1}{n} \sum_{j=0}^{n-1} \log T^j x = -\frac{1}{\log 2} \int_0^1 \frac{\log t}{1 + t} dt = \lim_{n \to \infty} \frac{\log q_n}{n}.$$

Integration by parts show

$$-\int_0^1 \frac{\log t}{1 + t} dt = \int_0^1 \frac{\log(1 + t)}{t} dt = \sum_{k=0}^{\infty} \int_0^1 \frac{t^k}{k + 1} dt$$

$$= \sum_{k=0}^{\infty} \frac{(-1)^k}{(k + 1)^2} = \frac{\pi^2}{12 \log 2}.$$

This value is called Lévy's constant.
Therefore we find

$$-\lim_{n \to \infty} \frac{\log \lambda(B(k_1, ..., k_n))}{n} = \lim_{n \to \infty} \frac{q_n^2}{n} = \frac{\pi^2}{6 \log 2}$$

and call this number the entropy of the continued fraction expansion.
We remark that for periodic algorithms with period length p the limit

$$-\lim_{n \to \infty} \frac{\log q_{np}}{np}$$

exists but its value depends on the quadratic irrational. However, in some sense the average taken over all quadratic irrationals again is just Lévy's constant (see [Faivre 1992]).
Another difficulty appears for β-expansions. If

$$B(\varepsilon_1, ..., \varepsilon_n) = \{x : \varepsilon_1(x) = \varepsilon_1, ..., \varepsilon_n(x) = \varepsilon_n\}$$

then clearly

$$\lambda(B(\varepsilon_1, ..., \varepsilon_n)) \le \beta^n.$$

Therefore

$$-\lim_{n \to \infty} \frac{\log \lambda(B(\varepsilon_1, ..., \varepsilon_n))}{n} \ge \beta.$$

Unfortunately there are "bad" cylinders such that

$$\lambda(B(\varepsilon_1, ..., \varepsilon_n)) < \beta^{-n}.$$

Since $\beta > 1$ one sees that every $x < 1$ is contained in infinitely many "full" cylinders which satisfy $\lambda(B(\varepsilon_1, ..., \varepsilon_n)) = \beta^{-n}$. Therefore if

$$-\lim_{n \to \infty} \frac{\log \lambda(B(\varepsilon_1, ..., \varepsilon_n))}{n}$$

exists its value must be $\log \beta$. In fact this is correct for almost all points $x \in [0, 1[$.

We will not present a crash course on entropy in probability theory (for more information we refer to [Billingsley 1965] or [Walters 1982]) but use a result from [Parry 1964a] as a definition. Let be an f-expansion be given. Assume that the map $Tx = f^{-1}x - \lfloor f^{-1}x \rfloor$ is ergodic and admits an invariant measure μ which is equivalent to Lebesgue measure λ then we define the entropy as

$$h(T) = \int_0^1 \log |T'x| d\mu(x).$$

Parry presents three examples.

1. $f(x) = x - \alpha$, α irrational, $0 < \alpha < 1$.
   This gives the map $Tx = x + \alpha - \lfloor x + \alpha \rfloor$. This map is called an irrational rotation since the map $\Psi e^{it} = e^{i(t+\alpha)}$ is a rotation of the circle $\mathbb{S}^1 = \{z \in \mathbb{C} : |z| = 1\}$. Since $T'x = 1$ we obtain $h(T) = 0$. Note that T is not ergodic if α is a rational number.

2. $f(x) = \frac{x}{\beta}$, $\beta > 1$, nonintegral
   Then the map $Tx = \beta x - \lfloor \beta x \rfloor$ gives the β-expansion and $T'x = \beta$ and $h(T) = \log \beta$.

3. $f(x) = \frac{x - \alpha}{\beta}$, $\beta > 1$, $0 < \alpha < 1$. Then

$$Tx = \beta x + \alpha - \lfloor \beta x + \alpha \rfloor.$$

The example $Tx = \beta x + \frac{3-\beta}{2} - \lfloor \beta x + \frac{3-\beta}{2} \rfloor$, $\beta = \frac{1+\sqrt{5}}{2}$ shows that there are cases without an equivalent invariant measure. If such a measure exists clearly $h(T) = \log \beta$.

If all cylinders of an f-expansion are full (this means $T^n B(k_1, ..., k_n) = B$) and Rényi's condition implies

$$- \lim_{n \to \infty} \frac{\log \lambda(B(k_1, ..., k_n))}{n} = h(T).$$

In this case

$$\omega(k_1, ..., k_n; x) \asymp \lambda(B(k_1, ..., k_n)).$$

If $x \in B(k_1, ..., k_n)$ then

$$f(k_1 + f(k_2 + ... + f(k_n + T^n x)...)) = x$$

and the chain rule shows

$$\omega(k_1, ..., k_n; T^n x) = \frac{1}{|(T^n)'x|} = \frac{1}{|T'x \cdot T'(Tx) \cdot ... \cdot T'(T^{n-1}x)|}.$$

Then the ergodic theorem is applied to the function $\log |T'x|$.

We remark that entropy is also connected with *Hausdorff dimension*. The appearance of logarithms in many results indicates such a connection.

Chapter 20

Hausdorff dimension

[Hausdorff 1918] was an important step in the development of measure theory. Here we consider his considerations on a new concept of *dimension* for linear sets and its application to sets which are constructed in a way similar to the *Cantor set*. Let $\lambda(x)$ be a continuous increasing function for $x > 0$ with $\lim_{n \to 0+} \lambda(x) = 0$ which is convex from above. Note that λ does not denote Lebesgue measure. Hausdorff used this letter to denote a generalization of *length*. The standard example is given by $\lambda(x) = x^\alpha$, $0 < \alpha \le 1$. It is proved that $2\lambda(x) > \lambda(2x)$.

Let (I_n), $n = 1, 2, 3, ...$, be a covering of the set A by intervals with length $d_n < \rho$ and form first

$$L_{\rho,\alpha}(A) = \inf\{\sum_{n=1}^{\infty} \lambda(d_n) : (I_n)_{n=1}^{\infty} \text{ covers } A\}$$

and then

$$L_\alpha(A) = \lim_{\rho \to 0} L_\rho(A).$$

If $0 < L_\alpha(A) < \infty$ then Hausdorff calls A a set of dimension $[\lambda(x)]$. His definition is slightly more narrow than later developments (see e. g. [Rogers 1998]). The essential difference is that the values 0 and $+\infty$ are admitted. Then it is easy to show that $L_\alpha(A) < +\infty$ implies $L_\beta(A) = 0$ for $\beta > \alpha$. Therefore there is a unique number σ such that $L_\alpha(A) = 0$ for $\alpha > \sigma$ and $L_\alpha(A) = +\infty$ for $\alpha < \sigma$. In fact, the calculation of $L_\alpha(A)$ is much more difficult than the determination of the dimension of a set. For sets defined by g-adic expansions which are similar to Cantor's set

[Wegmann 1971] reduced the evaluation to a combinatorial problem.

Let $\xi_0, \xi_1, \xi_2, \ldots$ be a sequence of positive numbers such that

$$\xi_0 > 2\xi_1, \xi_1 > 2\xi_2, \xi_2 > 2\xi_3, \ldots.$$

We start with the interval $[0, \xi_0]$ and first delete the middle open interval $]\xi_1, \xi_0 - \xi_1[= \beta(\frac{1}{2})$. The two closed intervals $[0, \xi_1]$ and $[\xi_o - \xi_1, \xi_0]$ remain. We now delete the middle open intervals of length $\xi_1 - 2\xi_2$ and call them $\beta(\frac{1}{4})$ and $\beta(\frac{3}{4})$ and so on. In this way every dyadic rational number $y \in]0, 1[$ is attributed an open interval $\beta(y)$. Then $A = [0, \xi_0] \setminus \bigcup_y \beta(y)$ is a perfect nowhere dense set which can be covered 2^n intervals of length ξ_n. Therefore

$$L(A) \leq \liminf_n 2^n \lambda(\xi_n).$$

If we choose ξ_n by the condition $2^n \lambda(\xi_n) = 1$ then $L(A) \leq 1$. This amounts to the iterative choice of $\xi_0, \xi_1, \xi_2, \ldots$ by the relation

$$\lambda(\xi_{n-1}) = 2\lambda(\xi_n) > \lambda(2\xi_n)$$

which implies $\xi_{n-1} > 2\xi_n$.
More difficult is to show that $L(A) \geq 1$. Between two intervals $\beta(\frac{k-1}{2^n})$ and $\beta(\frac{k}{2^n})$ lies an interval $]u(\frac{k-1}{2^n}), v(\frac{k}{2^n})[$ of length ξ_n. If for dyadic rationals $y < \eta$ then for the two intervals $\beta(y)$ and $\beta(\eta)$ the inequality

$$\lambda(u(\eta) - v(y)) \geq \eta - y$$

holds. This affords a lengthy discussion of several cases. Now let the set A be covered by open intervals α_n with length $< \rho$ such that

$$\sum_n \lambda(\alpha_n) < L_\rho + \varepsilon.$$

Then by Borel's theorem only finitely many intervals of the given covering are needed and we can replace these intervals by closed intervals in the set $[0, \xi_0]$. If two of them have a point in common then we use the inequality

$$\lambda(x_1 + x_2) < \lambda(x_1) + \lambda(x_2).$$

Hausdorff proves this inequality for his function $\lambda(x)$. It would be easy if we suppose $\lambda'(x)$ is decreasing. Last but not least, if such an interval intersects with a "deleted" interval $\beta(y)$ but does not contain it we can drop the intersection. Then there remain $n + 1$ intervals $\alpha_0, \alpha_1, \ldots, \alpha_n$

which together with some "deleted" intervals $\beta_1, \beta_2, ..., \beta_n$ cover $[0, \xi_0]$. If $\beta_j = \beta(y_j)$ we find $\lambda(\alpha_0) \geq y_1$, $\lambda(\alpha_1) \geq y_2 - y_1$, ..., $\lambda(\alpha_{n-1}) \geq y_n - y_{n-1}$, $\lambda(\alpha_n) \geq 1 - y_n$. Hence

$$L_\rho(A) + \varepsilon > \sum_s \lambda(\alpha_s) \geq 1$$

which gives $L(A) \geq 1$.

As an example Hausdorff takes $\lambda(x) = x^p$, $0 < p < 1$, and $\xi_n = \xi^n$ where $\xi^p = \frac{1}{2}$. This gives the dimension

$$p = \frac{\log 2}{-\log \xi}.$$

For the classical Cantor set we have $\xi_n = 3^{-n}$ and therefore we find its dimension

$$p = \frac{\log 2}{\log 3}.$$

An interesting account on such sets and their connection to Fourier series is [Kahane & Salem 1994].

For g-adic expansions one can investigate the dimension of the set $A(g, S)$ of real numbers $x \in [0, 1]$ whose g-adic expansion $g \geq 3$ contains only the digits in a subset $S = \{\varepsilon_1, \varepsilon_2, ..., \varepsilon_r\}$. Volkmann wrote a series of papers about this and more general problems (see [Volkmann 1956]). We mention that this dimension is given as

$$\dim A(g, S) = \frac{\log r}{\log g}.$$

The paper [Besicovitch 1934] refers to the following result of [Hardy & Littlewood 1914]. Denote by $P(x, n)$ the sum of the first n figures of the number x, $0 < x < 1$, then the inequality

$$\left| P(x, n) - \frac{n}{2} \right| < \sqrt{n \log n}$$

is ultimately satisfied almost everywhere in $[0, 1]$. To say it differently: If $x = \sum_{i=1}^{\infty} \frac{\varepsilon_i}{2}$ is the 2-adic expansion and $P(x, n) = \sum_{i=1}^{n} \varepsilon_i$ then for almost every $x \in [0, 1]$ there is an $n_0 = n_0(x)$ such that $|P(x, n) - \frac{n}{2}| < \sqrt{n \log n}$ for all $n \geq n_0$. The final answer to inequalities of this type was given in [Khintchine 1924], the *law of the iterated algorithm*. Besicovitch is interested in the set

$$E_p = \{x : \limsup_n \frac{P(x,n)}{n} \leq p < \frac{1}{2}\}.$$

If ρ is satisfied by the equation

$$2^\rho = \frac{1}{p^p q^q}, \; p + q = 1,$$

then $\dim E_p = \rho$.

Since at Besicovitch's time the notion of *entropy* was not common in metrical number theory the more suggestive formula

$$\rho = \frac{p \log p + q \log q}{\log 2}$$

was not used.

In [Jarník 1929] the author proves the following theorem. Let $\alpha \geq 2$ be a given real number and P_α denote the set of real numbers such that the inequality

$$\left| x - \frac{p}{q} \right| < \frac{1}{q^\alpha}$$

has infinitely many solutions in integers p and q, then $\dim P_\alpha = \frac{2}{\alpha}$. In [Jarník 1928] various sets which are defined by continued fractions are considered. Let $\mathcal{M}_\alpha$ be the set of all numbers

$$x = \cfrac{1}{a_1 + \cfrac{1}{a_2 + ...}}$$

such that $a_n \leq \alpha$ for all $n \geq 1$. Then

$$\dim \mathcal{M}_2 > \frac{1}{4}.$$

If $\alpha > 8$ then

$$1 - \frac{4}{\alpha \log 2} \leq \dim \mathcal{M}_\alpha \leq 1 - \frac{1}{8\alpha \log \alpha}.$$

The gap $3 \leq \alpha \leq 8$ is due to the method. From this it follows that the set of all numbers with bounded partial quotients $\mathcal{M}_\infty = \bigcup_\alpha \mathcal{M}_\alpha$ satisfies

$$\mathcal{M}_\infty = 1.$$

We will give a sketch of proof of the last result. Let $I(a_1, ..., a_n) = \{x : a_1(x) = a_1, ..., a_n(x) = a_n\}$ be a cylinder of rank n. Its closure $\overline{I(a_1, ..., a_n)}$ is called a *long interval*. Define

$$V_n = \bigcup_{1 \leq a_1, ..., a_n \leq \alpha} I(a_1, ..., a_n) \text{ and } \mathcal{N}_\alpha = \bigcap_{j=1}^\infty V_j.$$

Clearly $\mathcal{N}_\alpha \setminus \mathbb{Q} = \mathcal{M}_\alpha$ and therefore $\dim \mathcal{N}_\alpha = \dim \mathcal{M}_\alpha$. Crucial are the following two lemmas. Here λ denotes the length of the intervals. If

$$\lambda(I(a_1, ..., a_n))^s \leq \sum_{k=1}^\alpha \lambda(I(a_1, ..., a_n, k))^s$$

then $\dim \mathcal{N}_\alpha \geq s$.
If

$$\lambda(I(a_1, ..., a_n))^s \geq \sum_{k=1}^\alpha \lambda(I(a_1, ..., a_n, k))^s$$

then $\dim \mathcal{N}_\alpha \leq s$.
The last assertion is easy to prove. It means

$$1 \geq \sum_{a_1=1}^\alpha \lambda(I(a_1))^s \geq \sum_{a_1=1}^\alpha \sum_{a_2=1}^\alpha \lambda(I(a_1, a_2))^s \geq \,....$$

If n is sufficiently great, say $\lambda(I(a_1, ..., a_n)) < \rho$ then we conclude that

$$L_s(\mathcal{N}_\alpha) \leq 1.$$

The first assertion is more difficult to prove because one has to consider any covering of $\mathcal{N}_\alpha$ by intervals. If $\mathcal{W}$ is a covering of the compact set $\mathcal{N}_\alpha$ by finitely many open intervals and $\mathcal{X}$ is a covering of $\mathcal{N}_\alpha$ with long intervals then the key is to prove the inequality

$$\Lambda(\mathcal{W}) \geq \frac{1}{4^s \alpha^{3s}} \Lambda(\mathcal{X}).$$

The main problem is to replace intervals of an arbitrary covering by cylinders.

An important development of these ideas was [Good 1941]. We quote two results. Let $A = \{\alpha_1, \alpha_2, ..., \alpha_k\}$ be a set of k positive integers. Let further $E = \{x : a_j(x) \in A \text{ for all } j \geq 1\}$ and $q_n(\alpha_1, ..., \alpha_n)$ be the denominator of the continued fraction

$$x = x = \cfrac{1}{a_1 + \cfrac{1}{a_2 + ... + \cfrac{1}{a_n}}}.$$

Then the equation

$$\sum_{a_1,...,a_n \in A} q_n(\alpha_1, ..., \alpha_n)^{-2s} = 1$$

has a unique root σ_n and the sequence σ_n tends to a limit σ when $n \to \infty$. Moreover $\dim E = \sigma$.

Let $F_\alpha = \{x : a_j(x) \geq \alpha \text{ for } j \geq 1\}$ then

$$\frac{1}{2} + \frac{1}{2\log(\alpha+2)} < \dim F_\alpha < \frac{1}{2} + \frac{\log\log(\alpha-1)}{2\log(\alpha-1)}.$$

[Eggleston 1951] is a very long paper on the dimension of various sets mainly in connection with Diophantine approximation. In the last section he generalizes the theorem of Besicovitch to M-adic expansions. Let

$$x = \sum_{j=1}^{\infty} \frac{e_j}{M^j},$$

$0 < p < \frac{M-1}{2}$, and $P(x, j) = \sum_{j=1}^{n} e_j$ then the sets

$$X = \{x : \limsup_{i \to \infty} \frac{P(x, i)}{i} \leq p\}$$

$$X = \{x : \liminf_{i \to \infty} \frac{P(x, i)}{i} \leq p\}$$

$$X = \{x : \lim_{i \to \infty} \frac{P(x, i)}{i} = p\}$$

Let r be the real root, $0 < r < 1$, of the equation

$$r^{M-1}(M - 1 - p) + r^{M-2}(M - 2 - p) + \ldots + r(1 - p) = p$$

and define ρ by the equation

$$M^\rho = \frac{1 + r + r^2 + \ldots + r^{M-1}}{r^p}$$

then $\dim X = \dim Y = \dim Z$.

Billingsley generalized Hausdorff dimension in a way which is adapted to problems connected with f-expansions (see [Billingsley 1960, 1961]). A further extension of this concept was given in [Wegmann 1968]. We follow the presentation given in [Billingsley 1965]. One can guess that the formal similarity between entropy and the dimension of sets calculated by Eggleston and others was influential. One considers r-adic expansions where $r \geq 2$ is an integer. One can restrict to coverings by cylinders due to the fact that cylinders of rank n are of the same size, namely r^{-n}. The situation is different for continued fractions (see [Kinney & Pitcher 1965]). Let μ be a probability measure on the Borel sets of the unit interval and put

$$\mu_\alpha(M, \rho) = \inf \sum_i \mu(v_i)^\alpha$$

where the infimum extends over all countable coverings by cylinders v_i with $\mu(v_i) < \rho$. In a similar way one finds

$$\lim_{\rho \to 0+} \mu_\alpha(M, \rho) = \mu_\alpha(M).$$

There is unique number α_0 such that $\mu_\alpha(M) = \infty$ if $\alpha < \alpha_0$ and $\mu_\alpha(M) = 0$ for $\alpha_0 < \alpha$. This number is denoted $\dim_\mu M$. As remarked, for r-adic expansions $\dim_\lambda$ equals Hausdorff dimension.

The main result is as follows. Let $u_n(x)$ be the cylinder of rank n which contains $x = \sum_{j=1}^\infty \frac{a_j(x)}{r^j}$. Let μ and ν be two probability measures. If

$$M \subseteq \{x : \lim_{n \to \infty} \frac{\log \nu(u_n(x))}{\log \mu(u_n(x))} = \delta\}$$

then

$$\dim_\mu = \delta \dim_\nu M.$$

If the numerator or the denominator equals $\log 0$ or $\log 1$ some obvious definitions hold. This theorem allows us to deduce Eggleston's result. We take $\mu = \lambda$ and ν be that probability measure which makes the sequence of digits an independent process with

$$\nu\{x : a_j(x) = k\} = p_k, \ 0 \le k < r.$$

Then

$$-\frac{1}{n} \log \nu(u_n(x)) = -\sum_{i=0}^{r-1} \frac{A(x, n, k)}{n} \log p_k$$

where $A(x, n, k)$ is the number of events $a_j(x) = k$ for $1 \le j \le n$. If M is the set of all x such that

$$\lim_{n \to \infty} \frac{A(x, n, k)}{n} = p_k$$

then clearly $\nu(M) > 0$ and therefore $\dim_\nu M = 1$. Since $\log \lambda(u_n(x)) = -\log r$ we obtain

$$\dim M = \dim_\lambda M = -\frac{\sum_k p_k \log p_k}{\log r},$$

the result in [Eggleston 1949]. The result on the Cantor set also follows easily. Suppose $r = 3$ and let ν be the measure under which the sequence of digits is independent. Let $\nu(a_n(x) = 0) = \nu(a_n(x) = 2) = \frac{1}{2}$ but $\nu(a_n(x) = 1) = 0$. Then we see that for all x from the Cantor set

$$\frac{\log \nu(u_n(x))}{\log \mu(u_x(x))} = \frac{\log 2}{\log 3}.$$

[Kinney & Pitcher 1965] extended Billingsley's approach to continued fractions. A crucial lemma is to show in which cases one can assure that $\dim E = \dim E_\lambda$. As pointed out $\dim E \le \dim E_\lambda$ is clear. The lemma is the following. If

$$\lim_{n \to \infty} \frac{1}{n} \log \lambda(B(k_1, ..., k_n)) = -H$$

exists for all $x \in E$, $k_j(x) = k_j$, $j \ge 1$, then $\dim E = \dim E_\lambda$. The proof is a little bit sketchy but a more general result [Wegmann 1968] confirms the lemma. From the results we mention the following. If

$$F_M = \{x : a_i(x) \ge M \text{ for all } i \ge 1\}$$

then

$$\dim F_M \ge \frac{\log M - 2 \int_0^1 \log t d\nu(t)}{-2 \int_0^1 \log t d\nu^*(t)}.$$

The measures ν and ν^* need some explanation. Here ν is the invariant density for the f-expansion related to $f(t) = \frac{M}{t}$ on $[M, \infty[$. In fact

$$\frac{d\nu}{d\lambda}(x) = \frac{1}{(\log(M+1) - \log M)(x + M)}.$$

This expansion corresponds to continued fractions of the form

$$x = \cfrac{M}{b_1 + \cfrac{M}{b_2 + \cfrac{M}{b_3 + \dots}}}, \ b_j \geq M, \ j \geq 1$$

(for a recent discussion of this type of continued fraction we refer to [Dajani & Kraaikamp & van der Wekken 2013]). Further let $\phi : [0, 1[\to F_M$ defined by assigning to x a regular continued fraction by

$$\phi(x) = \cfrac{1}{b_1 + \cfrac{1}{b_2 + \cfrac{1}{b_3 + \dots}}}.$$

Then ν^* is defined as $\nu^*(E) = \nu(\phi^{-1} E)$.

[Billingsley & Henningsen 1975] compute the Hausdorff dimension of sets defined by the frequencies of the sequences

$$(a_1(x), a_2(x), \dots).$$

One of their results considers the set $E = \{x : 1 \leq a_j(x) \leq r\}$. They introduce the probabilities

$$p(i_1, \dots, i_k) = q_k(i_1, \dots, i_k)^{-2s}$$

where

$$\sum_{1 \leq 1_1, \dots, i_k \leq r} q_k(i_1, \dots, i_k)^{-2s} = 1$$

and introduce

$$\alpha_k = \sup \frac{-\sum p(i_1, \dots, i_k) \log p(i_1, \dots, i_k)}{2 \sum p(i_1, \dots, i_k) \log q(i_1, \dots, i_k)}.$$

Then $\lim_{k \to \infty} \alpha_k = \dim E$.

Chapter 21

Multidimensional generalizations

The frame is the following (see [Waterman 1970]). Let A be a convex region in $\mathbb{R}^n$ and $F : A \to]0,1[^n$ be a bijective map such that the Jacobian $J(F; x)$ has continuous components and $J(F; x) \neq 0$ almost everywhere. Let $D = F^{-1}$ the inverse map. A sequence of integer vectors and points is defined in the following way.

$$a^1(x) = \lfloor D(x) \rfloor,\ \delta^1(x) = D(x) - a^1(x)$$

$$\ldots$$

$$a^k(x) = \lfloor D(\delta^{k-1}(x)) \rfloor,\ \delta^k(x) = D(\delta^{k-1}(x)) - a^k(x)$$

$$\ldots$$

where $\lfloor z \rfloor = (\lfloor z_1 \rfloor, ..., \lfloor z_n \rfloor)$ for $z = (z_1, ..., z_n)$. If $\delta_j^k(x) = 0$ for some $j \in \{1, 2, ..., n\}$ the algorithm stops. Therefore we put

$$B = \{x : \delta^k(x) \neq o,\ \text{for all}\ k \geq 1\}$$

and assume $\lambda(B) = 1$. Then cylinders are defined as usual

$$B^\nu = B(k^1, ..., k^\nu) = \{x \in B : a^j(x) = k^j, 1 \leq j \leq \nu\}.$$

From the definitions we obtain

$$x = F(a^1(x) + F(a^2(x) + ... + F(a^\nu(x) + \delta^\nu(x))...)).$$

The following assumptions which go back to [Rényi 1957] and [Schweiger 1964, 1965] are made. Let $f^\nu : \delta^\nu B^\nu \to B^\nu$ the inverse branch of δ^ν restricted to B^ν then there is a constant $C > 0$ such that

$$\sup_{t \in \delta^\nu B^\nu} |J(f_\nu; x)| \leq C \inf_{t \in \delta^\nu B^\nu} |J(f_\nu; x)|,$$

the so-called *Rényi's condition*. Furthermore there is an $L > 0$ such that

$$\lambda(\delta^\nu B^\nu) \geq L > 0$$

for all cylinders with positive measure (*L-condition*) and there are sufficiently many proper cylinders of order $\nu + 1$ contained in B^ν such that their union $\widehat{B}^{\nu+1}$ satisfies

$$\lambda(\widehat{B}^{\nu+1}) \geq q\lambda(B^\nu)$$

for some $q > 0$ (*q-condition*). We remind the reader that a cylinder is called *proper* (or *full*) if $\delta^\nu B^\nu = B$.

Waterman gives several criteria that $\bigcap_{\nu=1}^\infty B^\nu(x) = \{x\}$. This property was later called *topological convergence*. Then the cylinders generate the σ-algebra of Borel sets. Here, $B^\nu(x)$ is the cylinder of rank ν which contains the point x.

Rényi's condition and the L-condition ensure the existence of an invariant probability measure μ which is absolutely continuous with respect to Lebesgue measure. If additionally the q-condition holds the measure μ is equivalent to λ. The condition $\bigcap_{\nu=1}^\infty B^\nu(x) = \{x\}$ for almost all $x \in B$, Rényi's condition and the q-condition suffice that the map δ is ergodic. Next Waterman uses *Rohlin's formula* to show that for F-expansions which satisfy more or less all the named conditions the equality

$$\lim_{\nu \to \infty} \frac{1}{\nu} \log \frac{1}{\mu(B^\nu(x))} = \int_B \log |J(D; t)| d\mu(t) = h(\delta)$$

holds where $h(\delta)$ denotes the *entropy* of the map δ (see the chapter on entropy). Furthermore the map δ is an *exact endomorphism* and is *mixing of all degrees*.

The following class of examples is presented. Let $M_1, M_2, ..., M_n$ be a fixed set of real numbers with $M_j \geq 1$ for $1 \leq j \leq n$ and define

$$F(x_1, ..., x_n) = \left(\frac{M_1}{x_n}, \frac{M_2 x_1}{x_n}, ..., \frac{M_n x_{n-1}}{x_n} \right)$$

where

$$x \in A = \{z : z_n \geq M_1, z_n \geq M_2 z_1, z_n \geq M_3 z_2, ..., z_n \geq M_n z_{n-1}\}.$$

Then we obtain

$$D(y_1, ..., y_n) = \left(\frac{M_1 y_2}{M_2 y_1}, \frac{M_1 y_3}{M_3 y_1}, ..., \frac{M_1 y_n}{M_n y_1}, \frac{M_1}{y_1} \right).$$

In a way similar to Jacobi-Perron algorithm (the case $M_1 = M_2 = ... = M_n = 1$) the map δ and its iterates are expressed by the use of matrices. It is said that a convergence proof [Perron 1907] is possible. Rényi's condition and the q-condition can be verified easily but the L-condition presents difficulties.

At least for $n = 2$ one can decide if the L-condition holds. The convex region $A = \{x : x_2 \geq M_1, x_2 \geq M_2 x_1\}$ is bounded by the straight lines $x_2 = M_1$, $x_1 = 0$, and $x_2 = M_2 x_1$. The map $\psi(x_1, x_2) = (M_1 x_1, M_1 x_2)$ shows that the system with parameters (M_1, M_2) is isomorphic to the system with parameters $(1, M_2)$. Therefore we can restrict to $M_1 = 1$. Let $Q(a_1, a_2)$ be the square $\{z : a_1 \leq z_1 < a_1 + 1, a_2 \leq z_2 < a_2 + 1\}$. Then $TB((a_1, a_2) + (a_1, a_2)) = Q(a_1, a_2) \cap A$. Therefore if M_2 is rational only finitely many images can appear. If M_2 is irrational the line $x_2 = M_2 x_1$ cuts out arbitrarily small pieces when it comes close to the point $(a_1 + 1, a_2 + 1)$ from below.

Another source for multidimensional F-expansions are generalizations of g-adic and β-adic expansions. The most common are complex digit expansions, expansions which use real matrices (often seen as endomorphisms of the d-dimensional torus) and complex continued fractions.

We shortly describe the work in [Fischer 1973]. The easiest way is to define directly the underlying map. Let A be a non-singular real $(d \times d)$-matrix and put $y = Ax$. Then the map is given as

$$Tx = T(x_1, x_2, ..., x_d) = (y_1 - k_1, ..., y_d - k_d)$$

where

$$k^1(x) = k^1 = (k_1, ..., k_d) = (\lfloor y_1 \rfloor, ..., \lfloor y_d \rfloor).$$

Then we have $k^{s+1} = k^1(T^s x)$.

Let $\Delta = |\det A|$. Let $\mathcal{Z}_n$ be the set of all cylinders of rank n. Then he defines

$$\mathcal{A}_n = \{B(k^1, ..., k^n) : T^n B(k^1, ..., k^n) = B\}$$

$$\mathcal{B}_n = \{B(k^1, ..., k^n) : B(k^1, ..., k^s) \in \mathcal{Z}_s \setminus \mathcal{A}_s \text{ for } 1 \le s < n\}$$
$$\mathcal{D}_n = \{B(k^1, ..., k^n) : B(k^1, ..., k^s) \in \mathcal{Z}_s \setminus \mathcal{A}_s \text{ for } 1 \le s \le n\}$$
$$\beta_n = \#\mathcal{B}_n, \delta_n = \#\mathcal{D}_n, B_n = \bigcup_{E \in \mathcal{B}_n} E, D_n = \bigcup_{E \in \mathcal{D}_n} E.$$

If $\phi_0(x) = 1$ and $\phi_i(x) = \Delta^{-i} \sum_{Ty=x} c_{D_i}(y)$ then $\eta(x) = \sum_{i=0}^{\infty} \phi_i(x)$ is an invariant density. One verifies easily the equation

$$\eta(x) = \sum_{Ty=x} \eta(y)\Delta^{-i}.$$

Then

$$\sigma(x) = \frac{\eta(x)}{\int_0^1 \eta(t)dt}$$

is a normalized density.

Fischer now makes some additional assumptions on the matrix A. Then he defines $h_0(x) = 1$ and

$$h_n(x) = \sum_{Ty=x} h_{n-1}(y)\Delta^{-1} = \sum_{T^n y=x} \Delta^{-n}.$$

His first result is a theorem of Kuzmin type. There are constants $C > 0$ and $\rho > 1$ such that

$$|h_n(x) - \sigma(x)| \le C\rho^{-n}.$$

Since the sets $B_1, B_2, ..., B_n$, and D_n form a partition of B one sees that for a given $x \in B$ there are β_1 points $z \in B_1$ with $Tz = x$, β_2 points $z \in B_2$ with $T^2 z = x$ and so on. At last there are $\Delta^n \phi_n(x)$ points $z \in D_n$ with $T^n z = x$. This leads to the equation

$$\Delta^n h_n(x) = \beta_1 \Delta^{n-1} h_{n-1}(x) + \beta_2 \Delta^{n-2} h_{n-2}(x) + ... + \beta_n h_0(x) + \Delta^n \phi_n(x)$$

or equivalently

$$h_n(x) = \beta_1 \Delta^{-1} h_{n-1}(x) + \beta_2 \Delta^{-2} h_{n-2}(x) + ... + \beta_n \Delta^{-n} h_0(x) + \phi_n(x).$$

The assumption on the matrix A is chosen to apply a theorem of renewal theory [Feller 1968], namely there are constants $M > 0$ and $K > 1$ such that

$$\delta_n \Delta^{-n} \le MK^{-n}, n \ge 1.$$

It turns out that the problem lies in the estimate of the number of "bad" cylinders δ_n. Fischer says that the following examples satisfy this assumption.

- $d = 1$, $A = \beta > 1$

- $d = 2$, $A = r + iq$, $\Delta = r^2 + q^2 > 4((\sqrt{2} + \sqrt{3})^2$ (see [Fischer 1972])

- $d \geq 2$, A be a symmetric matrix and its eigenvalues are greater than $d2^{d+1}$ (see [Philipp 1967]).

The mentioned theorem from renewal theorem deals with two sequences of real numbers (p_n) and (a_n) and a third sequence defined as

$$u_0 = a_0, \; u_n = p_1 u_{n-1} + \ldots + p_n u_0 + a_n.$$

Furthermore let

$$m = \sum_{k=1}^{\infty} k p_k = \sum_{n=0}^{\infty} \sum_{k=n+1}^{\infty} p_k.$$

Under some assumptions one finds

$$\left| u_n - \frac{1}{n} \sum_{k=0}^{\infty} a_k \right| < C\beta^{-n}$$

for some $\beta > 1$. This theorem is applied to $p_n = \beta_n \Delta^{-n}$, $a_n = \phi_n(x)$, and $u_n = h_n(x)$. Note that

$$\eta(x) = \sum_{k=0}^{\infty} \phi_k(x)$$

and

$$\sum_{k=0}^{\infty} k \beta_k \Delta^{-k} = \int_0^1 \eta(t)dt.$$

As just outlined the work on multidimensional F-expansions and multidimensional continued fractions inspired subsequent work on ergodic properties of maps. Out from many papers we mention [Ito & Yuri 1987] and [Yuri 1986]. They used the *finite range condition* which says that there are only finitely many sets which appear as images $\delta^\nu B(k^1, ..., k^\nu)$. This condition clearly implies the L-condition.

An amazing story in this connection is related to *Kuzmin's theorem*. More on its history was mentioned in another chapter. This theorem is crucial for results on the *mixing* behavior of the map. The attempt to generalize this theorem to multidimensional F-expansions is a history full of failures. The paper [Schweiger 1968b] tried to generalize Kuzmin's theorem to Jacobi-Perron algorithm. Waterman did the same for multidimensional F-expansions and obtained a convergence rate $O(\sigma(\sqrt{n})) + e^{-\gamma\sqrt{n}}$. In another paper [Schweiger 1968a] a first attempt was made to reach the convergence rate $O(\sigma(n))$ where $\sigma(n)$ denotes the supremum over the diameters of the cylinders of rank n. For continued fractions this would mean $O((\frac{3-\sqrt{5}}{2})^n)$ but [Wirsing 1973/74] later gave a better and even optimal rate of convergence. However, Schweiger's proof contained a serious flaw. On the other side, the new idea was to work with Cauchy's convergence criterion and therefore no assumption on the unknown invariant density was needed. Then a corrigendum was published [Schweiger 1969] but it contained another error which can be outlined as follows. We use the *transfer operator* A which is defined by the equation

$$\int_{T^{-1}E} \psi d\lambda = \int_E \psi d\lambda.$$

Note that a function h is an invariant density if and only if $Ah = h$. Let f be a positive Lipschitz function, h the invariant density, and put

$$0 < g_0 f < h < G_0 f$$

for some constants g_0 and G_0. Then iteration of the transfer operator A gives

$$0 < g_1(A^s f) < h < G_1(A^s f)$$

with $g_1 = g_0\alpha(s) + \beta(s)$, $G_1 = G_0\alpha(s) + \delta(s)$. The shape of the quantities $\alpha(s)$, $\beta(s)$, and $\delta(s)$ is not important for the type of error. Then the iteration was repeated but starting with

$$0 < g_1 f < h < G_1 f.$$

However, it is not clear if this inequality is correct! In this way the rate $O(\sigma(s))$ was obtained. Adriana Berechet and Marius Iosifescu detected this error some twenty years after the appearance of [Schweiger 1969]. Unfortunately this error was copied in some other papers. If one uses the correct statement

$$0 < g_1(A^s f) < h < G_1(A^s f)$$

then further iteration gives

$$0 < g_2(A^{2s} f) < h < G_1(A^{2s} f)$$

and so on. This gives essentially Kuzmin's rate $O(\sigma(\sqrt{n}))$. This was outlined in [Schweiger 2000]. In the meantime a quite different proof for the rate $O(\sigma(s))$ was proposed [Schweiger 2011]. Further results can be found in [Berechet 2001a, 2001b].

However, one must point out that for conclusions about the qualitative mixing behavior of F-expansions the weaker rate is sufficient. Furthermore, exponentially fast mixing has been proved by other authors by the use of different methods (see the chapter on Kuzmin's theorem).

Chapter 22

Chaos Theory

In the last decades *chaos theory* became very popular. Since some of its leading ideas are connected with f-expansions we give a short account. The so-called *quadratic family*

$$F(x, \mu) = \mu x(1 - x), \ \mu \geq 0$$

is one of the starting points for *chaos theory*. Chaos Theory is a cover term for several investigations which have a long history and is rooted in *iteration theory*. The concepts of *backward iteration* and *itinerary* are very similar to f-expansions. From the by-now long list of books we mention [Devaney 1987] and [Boyarski & Góra 1997].

Let us return to the quadratic family. An almost equivalent approach (for $\mu \geq 2$) is to consider the family of maps

$$P(x, a) = x^2 - a, \ a > -\frac{1}{4}.$$

If one uses the map $\phi(x) = Ax + \frac{1}{2}$, $A = \frac{1-\sqrt{1+4a}}{4a}$ and $\mu = 1 + \sqrt{1 + 4a}$ then one sees that

$$F(\phi(x), \mu) = \phi(P(x, a)).$$

It is amazing that such an innocent looking family of functions is the starting point for many investigations. If one replaces the real variable x by the complex variable z then one lands in the realm of *complex dynamics* ([Beardon 1991], [Steinmetz 1993], [Alexander et al. 2012]; see also the collective volume [Schleicher 2009] which presents a lot of recent results).

A basic idea centers around the appearance of *fixed points*. Let T : $B \to B$ be a given map. A point x is called a fixed point of (minimal) order n if the points $x, Tx, ..., T^{n-1}x$ are different but $x = T^n x$. The set $\{x, Tx, ..., T^{n-1}x\}$ is called a *cycle* of (minimal) order n. Hence a periodic decimal expansion is just a fixed point for the map $Tx = 10x - \lfloor 10x \rfloor$ and a periodic continued fraction a fixed point for the map $Tx = \frac{1}{x} - \lfloor \frac{1}{x} \rfloor$.

We look shortly at the map $Tx = P(x, a)$. If $1 + 4a < 0$ then this map has no real fixed point. If $1 + 4a = 0$ a first fixed point $\xi = \frac{1}{2}$ appears. It is called an *indifferent* fixed point because $|T'\xi| = 1$. If $1 + 4a > 0$ then there are 2 fixed points

$$\xi^+ = \frac{1 + \sqrt{1 + 4a}}{2} \text{ and } \xi^- = \frac{1 - \sqrt{1 + 4a}}{2}.$$

Since $T'\xi^+ > 1$ the first fixed point is called *repulsive*. The other fixed point is called *attractive* as long as $-1 < T'\xi^-$. If $a = \frac{3}{4}$ the we see that $T'\xi^- = -1$, the fixed point becomes indifferent. If $a > \frac{3}{4}$ then the fixed point ξ^- is also repulsive but a cycle of order 2 is born, namely $\{\frac{-1+\sqrt{4a-3}}{2}, \frac{-1-\sqrt{4a-3}}{2}\}$. This birth of fixed points is a fascinating entrance to chaos theory. A remarkable result says that if T is a continuous real map on an interval and T has a fixed point of order 3 then T has fixed points of all orders. This result is valid only for dimension $d = 1$. A rotation around the angle of $120°$ clearly would be a counterexample. An easy proof can be founde in [Li & Yorke 1975], but much more has been proved in [Sharkovskii 1964] (a readable account of Sharkovskii's theorem can be found in [Devaney 1987] or [de Melo & van Strien 1993]). It can be shown by an elementary but long calculation that the first cycle of length 3 is born at $a = \frac{7}{4}$. The condition $T^3 x = x$ leads to the equation

$$x^8 - 4ax^6 + (6a^2 - 2a)x^4 + (-4a^3 + 4a^2)x^2 - x + a^4 + 2a^3 + a^2 - a = 0.$$

Since the fixed points ξ^+ and ξ^- satisfy this equation we divide through $x^2 - x - a$ and find

$$x^6 + x^5 + (1 - 3a)x^4 + (1 - 2a)x^3 + (1 - 3a + 3a^2)x^2$$

$$+(1 - 2a + a^2)x + 1 - a + 2a^2 - a^3 = 0.$$

If $a = \frac{7}{4}$ we see that

$$x^6 + x^5 - \frac{17}{4}x^4 - \frac{5}{2}x^3 + \frac{79}{16}x^2 + \frac{9}{16}x + \frac{1}{64} = \left(x^3 + \frac{1}{2}x^2 - \frac{9}{4}x - \frac{1}{8}\right)^2.$$

Let B be a partitioned into sets $A_0, A_1, A_2, \ldots$. The *itinerary* of a point $x \in B$ is the sequence $\sigma(x) = s_0 s_1 s_1 \ldots$ where $s_j = k$ if $T^j x \in A_k$ (which is reminiscent to a sequence of digits). One can see the itinerary as a sequence of digits which describes the orbit of the point x. Let us assume that the partition consists of two sets A_0 and A_1. The space $\Sigma_2 = \{0,1\}^{\aleph_0}$ is the set of all sequences $s = s_0 s_1 s_1 \ldots$ with $s_j \in \{0,1\}$. The distance

$$\rho(s,t) = \sum_{i=0}^{\infty} \frac{s_i - t_i}{2}$$

gives Σ_2 the structure of a metric space. Note that the shift

$$\tau(s_0 s_1 s_1 \ldots) = s_1 s_2 s_3 \ldots.$$

is a continuous map on the metric space Σ_2. We consider the map $Tx = \mu x(1-x)$ on $[0,1]$ for $\mu > 4$. Then the set

$$\Lambda = \{x : T^n x \in [0,1] \text{ for all } n \geq 0\}$$

is a kind of Cantor set (see the chapter on dimension). We take $A_0 = \Lambda \cap [0, \frac{1}{2}]$ and $A_1 = \Lambda \cap [\frac{1}{2}, 1]$ as the partition. Then one can prove that for $\mu > 2 + \sqrt{5}$ the map σ is a *homeomorphism* (see [Devaney 1987]). This illustrates the idea of *symbolic dynamics* and *topological conjugacy*.

Another idea is to look for invariant measures. Again we consider the map $Tx = \mu x(1-x)$. If $\mu = 4$ it is known (and can be verified by an elementary calculation) that

$$h(x) = \frac{1}{\sqrt{x(1-x)}}$$

is the density of an invariant measure. If $\mu > 4$ then $F(\frac{1}{2}, \mu) = \frac{\mu}{4} > 1$ lies outside the interval $[0,1]$ and as outlined before iteration leads to a Cantor set. Therefore the case $\mu < 4$ is more interesting for the search of an invariant measure. Since in this case $F(\frac{1}{2}, \mu) = \frac{\mu}{4} < 1$ only a subset of $[0,1]$ can admit an invariant measure. [Ruelle 1977] was the first result in this area. If $0 < \mu < 4$ is the real root of the equation $(x-2)^2(x+2) = 16$ then $Tx = \mu x(1-x)$ admits an invariant density on the interval $[\frac{1}{a}, 1 - \frac{1}{a}]$. The key to this result is the observation

$$T^2 [\frac{1}{a}, \frac{a}{4}] = [\frac{1}{a}, \frac{a}{4}].$$

From the many further results in this direction we mention [Pianigiani 1979] and [Jakobson 1980].

Chapter 23

References

Aaronson, J. 1997 *An introduction to infinite ergodic theory* Mathematical Surveys and Monographs, 50. American Mathematical Society, Providence, RI, 1997

Adler, R. L. 1973 F-expansions revisited. *Recent Advances in Topological Dynamics. LNM* 318, Berlin Heidelberg New York: Springer Verlag, 1–5

Adler, R. L. & T. J. Rivlin, T. J. 1964 Ergodic and mixing properties of Chebyshev polynomials. *Proc. Amer. Math. Soc.* 15 (1964), 794–796

Adler, R. L. & B. Weiss 1973 The ergodic infinite measure preserving transformation of Boole. *Israel J. Math.* 16 (1973), 263–278.

Alexander, D. S., F. Iavernaro & A. Rosa 2012 *Early Days in Complex Dynamics* American Mathematical Society 2012

Alufohai, I. C. 1981 A class of weak Bernoulli transformations associated with representations of real numbers. *J. London Math. Soc.* (2) 23 (1981), 295–302

Arnold, V. I. & A. Avez 1967 Problèmes ergodiques de la mécanique classique. Monographies Internationales de Mathématiques Modernes, No. 9 Gauthier-Villars, Éditeur, Paris 1967

Arnoux, P. & A. Nogueira 1993 Mesures de Gauss pour des algorithmes de fractions continues multidimensionnelles. *Ann. Sci. École Norm. Sup.* (4) 26 (1993), 645–664

Babenko, K. I. 1978 = К. И. Бабенко A problem of Gauss. Dokl. Akad. Nauk SSSR 238 (1978) , 1021–1024 (= *Soviet Math. Dokl.* 19 (1978), 136–140)

Bagemihl, F. & J. R. McLaughlin 1966 Generalization of some classical theorems concerning triples of consecutive convergents to simple continued fractions *J. Reine Angew. Math.* 221 (1966), 146–149

Bailey, D. H. & P. B. Borwein & S. Plouffe 1997 On the rapid computation of various polylogarithmic constants *Mathematics of Computation* 66 (1997), 903–913

Bailey, D. H., J. M. Borwein, A. Mattingly &c. 2013 The computation of previously inaccessible digits of π^2 and Catalan's constant.*Notices of the AMS* 60 (2013), 844–854

Balkema, A. A. 1968 Hoofdstuk V, *Seminarium Getal en Kans* 1967/68, 45-66. Mathematisch Instituut Amsterdam

Banach, S. 1932 *Théorie des opérations linéaires* Monografje Matematyczne I, Warszawa 1932.

Bankier, J. D. & W. Leighton 1942 Numerical continued fractions. *Amer. J. Math.* 64 (1942), 653–668.

Beardon, A. F. 1991 *Iteration of Rational Functions* Springer-Verlag 1991

Berechet, A. 2001a Perron-Frobenius operators acting on BV(I) as contractors. *Ergodic Theory Dynam. Systems* 21 (2001), 1609–1624.

Berechet, A. 2001b A Kuzmin-type theorem with exponential convergence for a class of fibred systems. *Ergodic Theory Dynam. Systems* 21 (2001), 673–688.

Berg, L. 1955 Allgemeine Kriterien zur Maßbestimmung linearer Punktmengen. *Math. Nachrichten* 14 (1955), 263–285

Berg, L. 1957 Maßbestimmung linearer Punktmengen. *Math. Nachrichten* 16 (1957), 195–205

Berg, L. 1958 Maßbestimmung linearer Punktmengen (Fortsetzung). *Math. Nachrichten* 17 (1958), 211–218

Bernstein,F. 1912 Über eine Anwendung der Mengenlehre auf ein aus der Theorie der säkularen Störungen herrührendesProblem. *Math. Ann.* 71 (1912), 417–439

Berthé, V. 2012 Numeration and discrete dynamical systems. Computing 94 (2012), 369–387

Besicovitch, A.S. 1934 On the sum of digits of real numbers represented in the dyadic system. (On sets of fractional dimensions II.) *Math. Ann.* 110 (1934), 321–330

Billingsley, P. & I. Henningsen 1974 Hausdorff dimension of some continued-fraction sets. *Z. Wahrscheinlichkeitstheorie und Verw. Gebiete* 31(1974/75), 163–173

Billingsley, P. 1965 *Ergodic theory and information.* John Wiley & Sons, Inc., New York-London-Sydney 1965

Billingsley, P. 1961 Hausdorff dimension in probability theory. II. *Illinois J. Math.* 5 (1961), 291–298

Billingsley, P. 1960 Hausdorff dimension in probability theory. *Illinois J. Math.* 4 (1960) 187–209

Bissinger, B. H. 1944 A generalization of continued fractions. *Bull. Amer. Math. Soc.* 50 (1944), 868–876

Bleicher, M. N. & P. Erdös 1976a Denominators of Egyptian fractions *J. Number Theory* 8 (1976), 157–168

Bleicher, M. N. & P. Erdös 1976b Denominators of Egyptian fractions II. *Illinois J. Math.* 20 (1976), 598–613

Bohl, P. 1909 Über ein in der Theorie der säkularen Störungen vorkommendes Problem *J. f. Mathematik* 135 (1909), 189–283

Bolyai, W. 1832 *Tentamen iuventutem studiosam in elementa matheseos purae elementaris ac sublimioris methodo intuitiva evidentiaque huic propria introducendi* (= An attempt to introduce interested young people to the elements of pure elementary and higher *mathematics by an intuitive method and genuine evidence.* Budapest 1832

Borel, E. 1909 Les probabilités dénombrables et leurs applications arithmétiques. Rend. Circ. Mat. Palermo 27 (1909), 246–271

Borwein, J., A. van der Poorten, J. Shallit & W. Zudilin 2014 *Neverending fractions. An introduction to continued fractions.* Cambridge University Press

Bowen, R. 1979 Invariant measures for Markov maps of the interval. *Comm. Math. Phys.* 69 (1979), 1–17

Boyarsky, A. & P. Góra 1997 *Laws of Chaos. Invariant Measures and Dynamical Systems in One Dimension* Boston.Basel.Berlin: Birkhäuser 1997

Brezinski, C. 1991 *History of Continued Fractions and Padé Approximants* Berlin Heidelberg New York: Springer-Verlag

Bugeaud, Y. 2012 *Distribution Modulo One and Diophantine Approximation* Cambridge University Press 2012

Burton, R. M., Kraaikamp, C. & Schmidt, T. A. 2000 Natural extensions for the Rosen fractions. *Trans. Amer. Math. Soc.* 352 (2000), 1277–1298

Cantor, G. 1869a Über die einfachen Zahlensysteme. *Zeitschrift für Mathematik und Physik* 14(1869), 121–128

Cantor, G. 1869b Zwei Sätze über eine gewisse Zerlegung der Zahlen in unendliche Produkte *Zeitschrift f. Mathematik und Physik* 14 (1869), 152–158

Cassels, J. W. S. 1957 *An introduction to Diophantine approximation.* Cambridge Tracts in Mathematics and Math. Phys.

Cassels, J. W. S. 1959 On a problem of Steinhaus about normal numbers. *Colloq. Math.* 7 (1959) 95–101

Champernowne, D. G. 1933 The construction of decimals normal in the scale of ten. *L. London Math. Soc.* 8 (1933), 254–260

Cigler, J. 1961 Ziffernverteilung in θ-adischen Brüchen. *Math. Z.* 75 (1960/1961), 8–13

Cohen, E. 1891 Note sur un développement etc. *Nouv. Ann Math* (3) 10 (1891), 508–514

Cohn, H. 1993 *Doeblin and modern probability.* Proceedings of the Conference "50 Years after Doeblin: Development in the Theory of Markov Chains, Markov Processes, and Sums of Random Variables" held at the University of Tübingen, Blaubeuren 1991. Edited by Harry Cohn. Contemporary Mathematics, 149. American Mathematical Society, Providence, RI

Dajani, K. & C. Kraaikamp 2002 *Ergodic theory of numbers.* Carus Mathematical Monographs, 29. Math. Ass. of America, Washington, DC, 2002

Dajani, K., C. Kraaikamp, & W. Steiner 2009 Metrical theory for α-Rosen fractions. *J. Eur. Math. Soc.* 11 (2009), 1259–1283

Dajani, K., C. Kraaikamp, &c. 2013 Ergodicity of N-continued fraction expansions. *J. Number Theory* 133 (2013), 3183–3204

Dajani, K., C. Kraaikamp & N. D. S. Langeveld 2015 Continued fraction expansions with variable numerators. *Ramanujan J.* 37 (2015), 617–639.

Davenport, H. & K. F. Roth 1955 Rational approximations to algebraic numbers. *Mathematika* 2 (1955), 160–167.

de Melo, W. & S. van Strien 1993 *One-dimensional dynamics.* Ergebnisse der Mathematik und ihrer Grenzgebiete. Springer-Verlag, Berlin, 1993.

Denjoy, A. 1936 Sur une formule de Gauss. *C. R. Acad. Sci., Paris* 202 (1936), 537–540

Devaney, R. L. 1987 *An Introduction to Chaotic Dynamical Systems.* Addison-Wesley Publishing Company

Dixon, J. D. 1970 The number of steps in the Euclidean algorithm. *J. Number Theory* 2 (1970), 414–422

Doeblin, W. 1940 Remarques sur la théorie métrique des fractions continues. Compositio Math. 7 (1940), 353–371

Doeblin, W. 1937 Thesis *Bull. Soc. Roumaine Sc.* 39 (1937), 57–115.

Doeblin, W.& R. Fortet 1937 Sur des chaînes à liaisons complètes. *Bull. Soc. math. France* 65 (1937), 132–148

Dunford, N. & D. S. Miller 1946 On the ergodic theorem. *Trans. Amer. Math. Soc.* 60 (1946), 538–549.

Eggleston, H. G. 1951 Sets of fractional dimensions which occur in some problems of number theory. *Proc. London Math. Soc.* (2) 54 (1952), 42–93

Eggleston, H. G. 1949 The fractional dimension of a set defined by decimal properties. *Quart. J. Math., Oxford* Ser. 20 (1949), 31–36.

Einsiedler, M. & T. Ward 2011 *Ergodic Theory with a View towards Number Theory.* Graduate Texts in Mathematics, 259. Springer-Verlag London, Ltd., London, 2011

Erdös, P, A. Rényi & P. Szüsz 1958 On Engel's and Sylvester's series. *Ann. Univ. Sci. Budapest. Eötvös. Sect. Math.* 1 (1958), 7–32

Escott, E. B. 1937 Rapid method for extracting a square root. *Amer. Math. Monthly* 44 (1937), 644-646

Everett, C. J. 1946 Representations for real numbers. *Bull. Amer. Math. Soc.* 52 (1946), 861–869

Faivre, C. 1992 Distribution of Lévy constants for quadratic numbers. *Acta Arith.* 61 (1992), 13–34

Feller, W. 1968 *An introduction to probability theory and its applications.* Vol. I. Third edition John Wiley & Sons, New York-London-Sydney 1968

Fischer, R. 1975 Sofic systems and graphs. *Monatsh. Math.* 80 (1975), 179–186.

Fischer, R. 1973 Mischungsgeschwindigkeit für Ziffernentwicklungen nach reellen Matrizen. *Acta Arith.* 23 (1973), 5–12

Fischer, R. 1972 Ergodische Eigenschaften komplexer Ziffernentwicklungen. *Österreich. Akad. Wiss. Math.-Natur. Kl. S.-B.* II 180 (1972), 49–68.

Fluch, W. 1986 Eine Verallgemeinerung des Kuzmin-Theorems. *Österreich. Akad. Wiss. Math.-Natur. Kl. Sitzungsber.* II 195 (1986), 325–339.

Galambos, J. 1976 *Representations of real numbers by infinite series.* Springer-Verlag Berlin . Heidelberg . New York

Gauss, C. F. 1812 Gauss an Laplace. In: *Gauss Werke X_1.* Georg Olms, Hildesheim. New York 1973

Gel'fond, A. O. 1959 = А. О. Гельфонд Об одном общем свойстве систем счисления. *Известия Академии Наук СССР. Серия математическая* 23 (1959), 809–814

Goldie, Ch. M. & R. L. Smith 1987 On the denominators in Sylvester's series. *Proc. London Math. Soc.* (3) 54 (1987), 445–476.

Good, I. J. 1941 The fractional dimensional theory of continued fractions. *Proc. Cambridge Philos. Soc.* 37 (1941), 199–228.

Gordin, M. I. 1971 = М. И. Гордин Exponentially fast mixing *Soviet Math. Dokl.* 12 (1971), 331–335

Gordin, M. I. 1968 Stochastic processes generated by number-theoretic endomorphims. *Soviet Math. Dokl.* 9 (1968), 1234–1236

Guthery, S. B. 1970 An inversion algorithm for one-dimensional F-expansions. *Ann. Math. Statist.* 41 (1970), 1472–1490

Halfant, M. 1977 Analytic properties of Rényi's invariant density. em Israel J. mathematics 27 (1977), 1–20

Halmos, P. R. 1950 *Measure Theory* D. Van Nostrand Company, Inc., New York, N. Y., 1950.

Hardy, G. H. & J. E. Littlewood 1914 Some problems of Diophantine approximations I. The fractional part of $n^k\theta$. *Acta Mathematica* 37(1914), 155–191

Harman, G. 1998 *Metric Number Theory.* Oxford: Clarendon Press.

Hartman, S. & E. Marczweski & C. Ryll-Nardzweski 1951 Théorèmes ergodiques et leurs applications. *Colloq. Math.* 2 (1951), 109–123

Hartono, Y., C. Kraaaikamp & F. Schweiger 2002 Algebraic and ergodic properties of a new continued fraction algorithm with non-decreasing partial quotients. *J. Théorie des Nombres de Bordeaux* 14 (2002), 497–516

Hausdorff, F. 1918 Dimension und äußeres Maß. *Math. Ann.* 79 (1918), 157–179

Hawkins, T. 1975 *Lebesgue's Theory of Integration* Chelsea Publishing Company 1975

Hecke, E. 1936 Über die Bestimmung Dirichletscher Reihen durch ihre Funktionalgleichungen *Math. Ann.* 112 (1936), 664–690

Heilbronn, H. 1969 On the average length of a class of finite continued fractions *Number Theory and Analysis (Papers in Honor of Edmund Landau)*, 87–96 Plenum, New York 1969

Hensley, D. 2006 *Continued Fractions* World Scientific 2006

Hlawka, E. 1984 *The theory of uniform distribution* Transl. from the German by Henry Orde. With a foreword by S. K. Zaremba. Topics and Texts in Mathematics, Vol. 1. Berkhamsted, Herts., England: A B Academic Publishers 1984

Holzer, L. 1928 Zur Bestimmung des Lebesgueschen Maßes linearer Punktmengen, deren Elemente durch systematische Entwicklungen gegeben sind *S. Ber. Akad. Wiss. Wien Math.-naturw. Klasse* 127 (1928), 421–453

Hopf, E. 1937 Hopf, E. *Ergodentheorie* Ergebn. Math. Grenzgeb. 5, Heft 2, Julius Springer, Berlin 1937

Hurwitz, A. 1891 Über die angenäherte Darstellung der Irrational-zahlen durch rationale Brüche. *Math. Ann.* 39 (1891), 279–284

Hurwitz, A. 1888 Über die Entwicklungen komplexer Größen in Kettenbrüche. *Acta Math.* 11 (1888), 187–200 (= Werke II, 72-83)

Ibragimov, I. A., Yu. V. Linnik & V. V. Petrov 1971 = **И. А. Ибрагимов, Ю. В. Линник и В. В. Петров** *Independent and stationary sequences of random variables*. Translation from the Russian edited by J. F. C. Kingman. Wolters-Noordhoff. Groningen

Iosifescu, M. 1994 On the Gauss-Kuzmin-Lévy theorem. I. *Rev. Roumaine Math. Pures Appl.* 39 (1994), 97–117

Iosifescu, M. 1992 A very simple proof of a generalization of the Gauss-Kuzmin-Lévy theorem on continued fractions and related questions. *Rev. Roumaine Math. Pures Appl.* 37 (1992),901–914

Iosifescu, M. 1977 A Poisson law for ψ-mixing sequences establishing the truth of a Doeblin's statement. *Rev. Roumaine Math. Pures Appl.* 22 (1977), 1441–1447

Iosifescu, M. & Kraaikamp, C. 2002 *Metrical theory of continued fractions.* Mathematics and its Applications, 547. Dordrecht: Kluwer Academic Publishers 2002

Iosifescu, M. & Ş. Grigorescu 1990 *Dependence with complete connections and its applications.* Cambridge Tracts in Mathematics, 96. Cambridge University Press, Cambridge

Ito, S. & M. Yuri 1987 Number theoretical transformations with finite range structure and their ergodic properties. *Tokyo J. Math.* 10 (1987), 1–32

Jacobi, C. G. J. 1835 De functionibus duarum variabilium quadrupliciter periodicis, quibus theoria transcendentium Abelian quibus theoria transcendentium Abelianarum innititur *J. Reine und Angewandte Mathematik* 13(1835), 55–78

Jacobs, K. 1960 *Neuere Methoden und Ergebnisse der Ergodentheorie* Ergebnisse der Mathematik und ihrer Grenzgebiete. Springer-Verlag, Berlin-Göttingen-Heidelberg 1960

Jacobsthal, E. & K. Knopp 1915 Bemerkungen über die Struktur linearer Punktmengen. *Sitzungsber. Berl. Math. Ges.* 14 (1915), 121–129

Jager, H. & C. Kraaikamp 1989 On the approximation by continued fractions. *Indag. Math.* 51 (1989), 289–307

Jager, H. and C. De Vroedt 1969 Lüroth series and their ergodic properties. *Indag. Math.* 31 (1969), 31–42

Jakobson, M. V. 1980 Construction of invariant measures absolutely continuous with respect to dx for some maps of the interval. *Global*

Theory of Dynamical Systems. LNM 819, Berlin · Heidelberg · New York: Springer Verlag, 246–257

Jarník, V. 1929 Diophantische Approximationen und Hausdorffsches Mass. Математический сборник = *Recueil math. Soc. math. Moscou* 36 (1929), 371–382

Jarník, V. 1928 Zur metrischen Theorie der diophantischen Approximationen. *Prace mat. fiz.* 36 (1928), 91–106

Jenkinson, O. & M. Pollicott 2000 Ergodic properties of the Bolyai-Rényi expansion. Indag. Math. (N.S.) 11 (2000), 399–418

Kac, M. 1959 *Statistical independence in probability, analysis and number theory* The Carus Mathematical Monographs, No. 12 MAA. Distributed by John Wiley and Sons, Inc., New York 1959

Kahane, J.-P. & R. Salem 1994 *Ensembles parfaits et séries trigonométriques* Second edition. With notes by Kahane, Thomas W. Körner, Russell Lyons and Stephen William Drury. Hermann, Paris 1994

Kakeya, S. 1924 On a generalized scale of notations. *Japan. J. Math.* 1 (1924), 95–108

Kalpazidou, S. 1985 On a random system with complete connections associated with the continued fraction to the nearer integer expansion. *Rev. Roumaine Math. Pures Appl.* 30 (1985), 527–537.

Kalpazidou, S., A. Knopfmacher & J. Knopfmacher 1991 Metric properties of alternating Lüroth series. *Portugal. Math.* 48(1991), 319–325

Kalpazidou, S., A. Knopfmacher & J. Knopfmacher 1990 Lürothtype alternating series representations for real numbers. *Acta Arithmetica* 55 (1990), 311–322

Karpenkov, O. 2013 *Geometry of Continued Fractions* Heidelberg et al.: Springer

Khintchine, A. Ya. 1963 = А. Я. Хинчин *Continued Fractions.* Groningen: Noordhoff

Khintchine, A. Ya. 1936 Zur metrischen Kettenbruchtheorie. *Compos. Math.* 3 (1936), 276–285

Khintchine, A. Ya. 1935 Metrische Kettenbruchprobleme. *Compos. Math.* 1 (1935), 361–382

Khintchine, A. Ya. 1932 Zu Birkhoffs Lösung des Ergodenproblems. *Math. Ann.* 107 (1932), 485–488

Khintchine, A. 1924 Über einen Satz der Wahrscheinlichkeitsrechnung. *Fund. math.* 6(1924), 9–20

Khintchine, A. 1923 Über dyadische Brüche. *Math. Z.* 18(1923), 109–116

Kinney, J. R. & T. S. Pitcher 1965 The dimension of some sets defined in terms of f-expansions. *Z. Wahrscheinkichkeitstheorie Verw. Gebiete* 4 (1965), 293–315

Knopfmacher, A. & J. Knopfmacher 1987 A new infinite product representation for real numbers. *Monatsh. Math.* *104* (1987), 29–44.

Knopp, K. 1926 Mengentheoretische Behandlung einiger Probleme der diophantischen Approximation und der transfiniten Wahrscheinlichkeiten. *Math. Ann.* 95 (1925), 409–426

Koksma, J. F. 1936 *Diophantische Approximationen.* Ergebnisse der Mathematik und ihrer Grenzgebiete. Berlin: Julius Springer

Kraaikamp, C. & Nakada, H. 2001 On a problem of Schweiger concerning normal numbers. *J. Number Theory* 86 (2001),330–340

Kraaikamp, C. & Nakada, H. 2000 On normal numbers for continued fractions. *Ergodic Theory Dynam. Systems* 20 (2000), 1405–1421

Kraaikamp, C. & I. Smeets 2011 Sharp bounds for symmetric and asymmetric Diophantine approximation. Chin. Ann. Math. Ser. B 32 (2011), no. 2, 303–320

Krieger, W. 1987 On sofic systems. II. *Israel J. Math.* 60 (1987), 167–176

Krieger, W. 1984 On sofic systems. I. *Israel J. Math.* 48 (1984), 305–330

Kronecker, L. 1884 Näherungsweise ganzzahlige Auflösung linearer Gleichungen. *Monatsber. der Königlich Preussischen Akademie der Wissenschaften zu Berlin vom Jahre* 1884, 1179-1193. 1271-1299 (= *Werke* III. Erster Halbband Berlin 1899, 47–109. Chelsea Publ. Co. , New York 1968)

Kuipers, L. & H. Niederreiter 1974 *Uniform distribution of sequences.* Pure and Applied Mathematics. Wiley-Interscience [John Wiley & Sons], New York-London-Sydney, 1974.

Kuzmin, R. O. = Р. О. Кузьмин 1928 Sur un problème de Gauss *Atti del Congresso Internazionale dei Matematici*: Bologna 3 - 10 settembre 1928 (VI). 6. Communicazioni sezione IV (A) - V - VII International Congress of Mathematicians, 1928, Bologna: Zanichelli 1932

Lacroix, Y. 1993 Metric properties of generalized Cantor products. *Acta Arith.* 63 (1993), 61–77

Lambert, J. H. 1761 Mémoire sur quelques propriétés remarquables des quantités transcendantes, circulaires et logarithmiques. *Histoire de l'Académie royale des sciences et belles-lettres (de Berlin)*, année 1761, 1768

Lamé, G. 1844 Note sur la limite du nombre de divisions dans la recherche du plus grand commun diviseur de deux nombres C. R. Acad. Sci. Paris 19(1844), 867–870

Lang, S. 1966 *Introduction to Diophantine Approximation* Addison-Wesley Publ. Comp. 1966

Lasota, A. & J. A. Yorke 1973 On the existence of invariant measures for piecewise monotonic transformations. *Trans. Amer. Math. Soc.* 186 (1973), 481–488

Lehmer, D. H. 1938 A cotangent analogue of continued fractions. *Duke Math. J.* 4 (1938), 323–340

Leighton, W. 1940 Proper continued fractions. *Amer. Math. Monthly* 47 (1940), 274–280

Lejeune Dirichlet, G. 1842 Verallgemeinerung eines Satzes aus der Lehre von den Kettenbrüchen nebst einigen Anwendungen auf die Theorie der Zahlen. *Bericht über die Verhandlungen der Königl.*

Preuss. Akademie der Wissenschaften Jg. 1842, 93-95 (= *Werke* Bd. I 1889. Chelsea Publ. Co., New York 1969

Lévy, P. 1929 Sur les lois de probabilité dont dépendent les quotients complets et incomplets d'une fraction continue. *Bull. de la Societé Math. France* 57 (1929), 178–194

Li, Tien Yien & J. A. Yorke 1975 Period three implies chaos. *Amer. Math. Monthly* 82 (1975), no. 10, 985–992

Lüroth, J. 1883 Über eine eindeutige Entwicklung von Zahlen in eine unendliche Reihe *Math. Ann.* 21 (1883), 411–424

Lucas, E. 1891 *Théorie des nombres*, t. I, Paris: Gauthier-Villars et Fils. 1891.

Martin, M. H. 1934 Metrically transitive point transformations *Bull. Am. Math. Soc.* 40, 606–612

Mayer, D. & G. Roepstorff 1987 On the relaxation time of Gauss's continued-fraction map I. The Hilbert space approach (Koopmanism). *J. Statist. Phys.* 47 (1987), 149–171

Mayer, D. & G. Roepstorff 1988 On the relaxation time of Gauss's continued-fraction map II. The Banach space approach (transfer operator method). *J. Statist. Phys.* 50 (1988), 331–344

Mazur, J. 2014 *Enlightening symbols. A short history of mathematical notation and its hidden powers* Princeton and Oxford: Princeton University Press

McKinney, T. E. 1907 Concerning a certain type of continued fractions depending on a variable parameter *Amer. J. Math.* 29 (1907), 213–278

Menninger, K. 1977 *Number words and number symbols : a cultural history of numbers.* Cambridge: The M.I.T. Press

Nakada, H. 1981 Metrical theory for a class of continued fraction transformations and their natural extensions. Tokyo J. Math. 4 (1981), 399–426

Nakada, H., S. Ito, & S. Tanaka 1977 On the invariant measure for the transformations associated with some real continued fractions. *KEIO Eng. Rep.* 30 (1977), 159–175

Natanson, I. P. 1955 & 1961 *Theory of functions of a real variable* Vol.I & Vol. II 1955. 1961 New York: Frederick Ungar

Nevanlinna, R. 1970 *Analytic Functions* Springer Verlag Berlin · Heidelberg · New York

Onicescu, O. & G. Mihoc 1935 Sur les chaînes de variables statistiques *Bull. Sc. Math.* (2) 59 (1935), 174–192

Oppenheim, A. 1953 On the representation of real numbers by products of rational numbers. *Quart. J. Math. Oxford* (2) 4 (1953), 303–307

Oppenheim, A. 1960 A note on continued fractions. *Canadian J. Math.* 12 (1960), 303–308

Oppenheim, A. 1971 Representations of real numbers by series of reciprocals of odd integers. *Acta Arith.* 18 (1971), 115–124

Parry, W. 1966 Symbolic dynamics and transformations of the unit interval. *Trans. Amer. Math. Soc.* 122(1966), 368–378.

Parry, W. 1964a On Rohlin's formula for entropy. *Acta Math. Acad. Sci. Hungar.* 15(1964), 107–113.

Parry, W. 1964b Representations for real numbers. *Acta Math. Acad. Sci. Hungar.* 15(1964), 95–105

Parry, W. 1960 On the β-expansions of real numbers. *Acta Math. Acad. Sci. Hungar.* 11(1960), 401Ũ-416

Perron, O. 1960 *Irrationalzahlen.* 4te Aufl. Göschens Lehrbücherei. Walter de Gruyter & Co., Berlin

Perron, O. 1957 *Die Lehre von den Kettenbrüchen. Bd. II. Analytisch-funktionentheoretische Kettenbrüche* 3te Aufl. B. G. Teubner Verlagsgesellschaft, Stuttgart

Perron, O. 1954 *Die Lehre von den Kettenbrüchen Bd I. Elementare Kettenbrüche.* 3te Aufl. B. G. Teubner Verlagsgesellschaft, Stuttgart

Perron, O. 1907 Grundlagen für eine Theorie des Jacobischen Kettenbruchalgorithmus. *Math. Ann.* 64 (1907), 1–76

Philipp, W. 1975/76 A conjecture of Erdő"s on continued fractions. *Acta Arith.* 28 (1975/76), 379–386.

Philipp, W. 1970 Some metrical theorems in number theory. II. *Duke Math. J.* 37 (1970), 447–458. Corrigendum *ibid.* 788

Philipp, W. 1969 Das Gesetz vom iterierten Logarithmus mit Anwendungen auf die Zahlentheorie. *Math. Ann.* 180 (1969), 75–94 Corrigendum *ibid.* 190 (1971), 338

Philipp, W. 1967 Mischungseigenschaften gewisser auf dem Torus definierter Endomorphismen. *Math. Z.* 101 (1967), 369–374.

Philipp, W. & O. P. Stackelberg 1969 Zwei Grenzwertsätze für Kettenbrüche. *Math. Ann.* 181 (1969), 152–156.

Pianigiani, G. 1979 Absolutely continuous invariant measures for the process $x_{n+1} = Ax_n(1 - x_n)$.*Boll. Un. Mat. Ital. A* (5) 16 (1979), 374–378

Pianigiani, G. 1980 First return map and invariant measures. *Israel J. Math.* 35 (1980), 32–48

Pierce, T. A. 1929 On an algorithm and its use in approximating roots of an algebraic equation. *Amer. Math. Monthly* 36 (1929), 523–525

Pollington, A. D. & W. Moran eds 1993 *Number Theory with an Emphasis on the Markoff Spectrum.* Lecture Notes in Pure and Applied Mathematics 147. New York: Marcel Dekker

Porter, J. W. 1975 On a theorem of Heilbronn. *Mathematika* 22 (1975), 20–28.

Rechard, O. W. 1950 The representation of real numbers. *Proc. Amer. Math. Soc.* 1 (1950), 674–681

Reichsöllner, C. J. 1989 Über die Größenordnung der invarianten Dichte von reellen Transformationen. Thesis Univ. Salzburg

Rényi, A.1962 A new approach to the theory of Engel's series. *Ann. Univ. Sci. Budap. Rolando Eötvös, Sect. Math.* 5 (1962), 25–32

Rényi, A. 1957 Representations for real numbers and their ergodic properties. *Acta Math. Acad. Sci. Hungar.* 8 (1957), 477–493

Rieger, G. J. 1977 Die metrische Theorie der Kettenbrüche seit Gauß. *Abh. Braunschweigische Wiss. Ges.* 27 (1977), 103–117

Rieger, C. J. 1978 Ein Gauss–Kuzmin–Levy – Satz für Kettenbrüche nach nächstem Ganzen. *Manuscripta Math.* 24 (1978), 437–448

Rivoal, T. 2007 Propriétés diophantiennes du développement en cotangente continue de Lehmer. *Monatsh. Math.* 150 (2007), 49–71

Rockett, A. M. & Szüsz, P. 1992 *Continued fractions.* Singapore: World Scientific

Rogers, C.A. 1998 *Hausdorff measures. With a foreword by K. Falconer.* Cambridge Mathematical Library. Cambridge: Cambridge University Press

Rohlin, V. A. 1961 = В. А. Рохлин Точные ендоморфизмы пространства Лебега *Известия Академии Наук СССР. Серия математическая* 25 (1961), 499–530

Roos, P. 1965 Iterierte Resttransformationen von Zahlendarstellungen. *Z. Wahrsch. Verw. Gebiete* 4 (1965), 45–63

Rosen, D. 1954 A class of continued fractions associated with certain properly discontinuous groups. *Duke Math. J.* 21 (1954), 549–563

Roth, K. F. 1955 Rational approximations to algebraic numbers *Mathematika* 2, 1–20, corrigendum p. 168

Rudolfer, S. M. 1971 Ergodic properties of linear fractional transformations mod one.*Proc. London Math. Soc.* (3) 23 (1971), 515–531

Ruelle, D. 1977 Applications conservant une mesure absolument continue par rapport à dx sur $[0, 1]$. *Comm. Math. Phys.* 55 (1977), 47–52

Ryde, F. 1951 Sur les fractions continues monotones nondécroissantes périodiques. *Ark. Mat.* 1 (1951), 409–420.

Ryll-Nardzwewski, C. 1951 On the ergodic theorems. II. Ergodic theory of continued fractions. *Studia Math.* 12 (1951), 74–79

Schleicher, D., ed. 2009 *Complex Dynamics.* Wellesley, Ma: A K Peters 2009

Schmidt, W. M. 1960 On normal numbers. *Pacific J. Math.* 10 (1960), 661–672

Schweiger, F. 2011 A new proof of Kuzmin's theorem. *Rev. Roumaine Math. Pures Appl.* 56 (2011), 229–234.

Schweiger, F. 2008 Inner symmetries for Moebius maps. *Österreich. Akad. Wiss. Math.-Natur. Kl. Sitzungsber.* II 217 (2008), 37–45

Schweiger, F. 2000 Kuzmin's theorem revisited. *Ergodic Theory Dynam. Systems* 20 (2000), 557–565

Schweiger, F. 1997 Arithmetical processes for building up number words. *Moderne Sprachen* 41/1 (1997), 75–88

Schweiger, F. 1995 *Ergodic Theory of Fibred Systems and Metric Number Theory.* Oxford Science Publications. The Clarendon Press, Oxford University Press, New York

Schweiger, F. 1969 Metrische Theorie einer Klasse zahlentheoretischer Transformationen: Corrigendum. *Acta Arith.* 16 (1969/1970), 217–219

Schweiger, F. 1968a Metrische Theorie einer Klasse zahlentheoretischer Transformationen. *Acta Arith.* 15 (1968), 1–18

Schweiger, F. 1968b Ein Kuzminscher Satz über den Jacobischen Algorithmus *J. Reine Angew. Math.* 232 (1968), 35–40

Schweiger, F. 1965 Metrische Sätze über den Jacobischen Algorithmus. *Monatsh. Math.* 69 (1965), 243–255

Schweiger, F. 1964 Geometrische und elementare metrische Sätze über den Jacobischen Algorithmus. *Österreich. Akad. Wiss. Math.-Natur. Kl. S.-B. II* 173 (1964), 59–92

Series, C. 2003 Why is there hyperbolic geometry in dynamics? In: E. Mezzettiet et al. (eds.), *European women in mathematics. Proceedings of the tenth general meeting*, Malta, August 24–30, 2001. River Edge, NJ: World Scientific. 191–207 (2003)

Series, C. 1985 The modular surface and continued fractions. *J. Lond. Math. Soc.*, II. Ser. 31 (1985), 69–80

Sharkovskii, A. 1964 = А. Шарковский Сосуществование циклов непрерывного преобразования прямой в себя (= Coexistence of cycles of a continuous map of the line itself) *Ukrain. Mat. Zhurn.* 16 (1964), 61–71

Sierpiński, W. 1911 O kilku algorytmach dla rozwijania liczb rzeczywistych na szeregi" in *C. R. Soc. Sci. Varsovie* 4 (1911), 56–77

Sierpiński, W. 1974 Sur quelques algorithmes pour développer les nombres réels en séries. *Selected Works. Travaux d'Analyse Mathématique*, 236–254

Sinai, Ya. G. 1994 *Topics in Ergodic Theory.* Princeton University Press, Princeton, N.J., 1994

Sloane, N. J. A. & A. D. Wyner eds 1993 *Claude Elwood Shannon. Collected Papers* The Institute of Electrical and Electronics Engineers, New York 1993

Spătaru, A. 1978 Independenţa stocastică a cifrelor unei f-expansiuni (= Stochastic independence of the digits of an f-expansion) *Stud. Cerc. Mat.* 30 (1978), 75–117

Spătaru, A. 1977 Some f-expansions producing stochastically independent digits. *Sankhyā: The Indian J. of Statistics.* Ser. A 39(1977), 160–169

Sprindžuk, V. G. 1979 = В. Г. Спринджук *Metric Theory of Diophantine Approximation* Washington, D. C.: V. H. Winston & Sons 1979

Steinmetz, N. 1993 *Rational Iteration* Berlin New York: Walter de Gruyter 1993

Stratemeyer, G. 1931 Entwicklung positiver Zahlen nach Stammbrüchen *Mitteilungen d. mathem. Seminars d. Universität Gießen* 20 (1931), 1–27

Sylvester, J. J. 1881 . On a point in the theory of vulgar fractions. *Amer. J. Math.* 3 (1880), 332–336. 388–390.

Szüsz, P. 1961 Über einen Kusminschen Satz. *Acta Math. Acad. Sci. Hung.* 12 (1961), 447–453

Tanaka, S. & Ito, S. 1981 On a family of continued fraction transformations and their ergodic properties. *Tokyo J. Math.* 4 (1981), 153–175

Thaler, M. 2002 A limit theorem for sojourns near indifferent fixed points of one-dimensional maps. *Ergodic Theory Dynam. Systems* 22 (2002), 1289–1312

Thaler, M. 1983 Transformations on [0, 1] with infinite invariant measures. *Israel J. Math.* 46 (1983), 67–96.

Thaler, M. 1980 Estimates of the invariant densities of endomorphisms with indifferent fixed points. *Israel J. Math.* 37 (1980), 303–314.

Tong, Jing Cheng 1983 The conjugate property of the Borel theorem on Diophantine approximation. *Math. Z.* 184 (1983), 151–153

Tong, Jing Cheng 1991 Diophantine approximation by continued fractions. *J. Austral. Math. Soc. Ser. A* 51 (1991), 324–330

Tong, Jingcheng 1994 Approximation by nearest integer continued fractions (II). *Math. Scand.* 74 (1994), 17–18

Tonkov, T. 1974/75 On the average length of finite continued fractions. *Acta Arith.* 26 (1974/75), 47–57.

Tran Vinh-Hien 1963 = **Чан Винг Хьен** Центральная предельная теорема для стационарных процессов, порожденных теоретикочисловыми ендоморфизмами. *Вестник Московского университета* No. 5–1963, 28–34

Tsuji, M. 1975 *Potential Theory in Modern Function Theory.* Reprinted by Chelsea Publ., New York

Vervaat, W. 1972 *Success epochs in Bernoulli trials with applications in number theory.* Mathematisch Centrum Amsterdam: Mathematisch Center Tracts 42

Volkmann, B. 1956 Über Hausdorffsche Dimensionen von Mengen die durch Ifferneigenschaften charakterisiert sind. V. *Math. Z.* 65 (1956), 389–413

von Plato, J. 1994 *Creating Modern Probability. Its mathematics, physics and philosophy in historical perspective.* Cambridge University Press 1004

Wagner, G. 1979 The ergodic behaviour of piecewise monotonic transformations. *Z. Wahrscheinlichkeitstheor. Verw. Geb.* 46 (1979), 317–324

Walters, P. 1982 *An Introduction to Ergodic Theory* New York Heidelberg Berlin: Springer-Verlag

Waterman, M.S. 1970 Some ergodic properties of multi-dimensional F-expansions. *Z. Wahrscheinlichkeitstheor. Verw. Geb.* 16, 77–103

Wegmann, H. 1968 Über den Dimensionsbegriff in Wahrscheinlichkeitsräumen von P. Billingsley. I, II. *Z. Wahrscheinlichkeitstheorie und Verw. Gebiete* 9 (1968), 216–221; ibid. 9 (1968), 222–231

Wegmann, H. 1971 Das Hausdorff-Mass von Cantormengen. *Math. Ann.* 193 (1971), 7–20

Weiss, B. 1973 Subshifts of finite type and sofic systems. *Monatsh. Math.* 77 (1973), 462–474

Weyl, H. 1916 Über die Gleichverteilung von Zahlen mod. Eins. *Math. Ann.* 77 (1916), 313–352

Wirsing, E. 1974 On the theorem of Gauss-Kusmin-Lévy and a Frobenius-type theorem for function spaces. Collection of articles dedicated to Carl Ludwig Siegel on the occasion of his seventy-fifth birthday. *Acta Arith.* 24 (1973/74), 507–528

Yuri, M. 1986 On a Bernoulli property for multidimensional mappings with finite range structure. *Tokyo J. Math.* 9 (1986), 457–485

87445336R00108

Made in the USA
Lexington, KY
25 April 2018